IONS IN SOLUTION

BY

Ronald Wilfrid

R. W. GURNEY, M.A., Ph.D.

Research Associate in the University of Bristol

DOVER PUBLICATIONS, INC.

NEW YORK

Published in the United Kingdom by Constable
and Company Limited, 10 Orange Street, London
W. C. 2.

This new Dover edition, first published in 1962,
is an unabridged and unaltered republication of
the work first published by the Cambridge University Press in 1936.

Library of Congress Catalog Card Number: 62-51393

Manufactured in the United States of America

Dover Publications, Inc.

180 Varick Street

New York 14, N. Y.

*This new Dover Edition is
dedicated to the memory of
Ronald W. Gurney
1898 - 1953*

CONTENTS

PREFACE

In the study of ions in gases a rapid advance was made after 1913, when Bohr directed attention to their electronic energies; in fact, our knowledge of atomic ions is already nearing completion. I have written the present book in the belief that a similar step forward may now be made for ions in solution, if their behaviour is interpreted by methods such as those which I have outlined here, and which I am elaborating in a subsequent volume.

I should like to express my thanks for the help which I have received from Professor N. F. Mott in discussions of some of these problems.

R. W. G.

Bristol 1936

CHAPTER I

§ 1. THE SOLVATION ENERGY OF AN ION

From a physical point of view any ion in solution is primarily an electric charge situated in a dielectric medium. Any positive or negative charge so situated has certain properties which are independent of its internal structure. We will accordingly begin by enquiring what information can be gleaned from the text-books on electrostatics. These text-books discuss the energy of the charge on any conductor. We may, therefore, begin by replacing our ion by a small conducting sphere of roughly the same size, having the same charge on its surface. The most important step is to enquire whether it is necessary to do work in order to remove the charge from the dielectric to a vacuum. We wish to compare the energy of the charge in the dielectric with the energy which the same charge would have when situated in a vacuum. If the charge is at rest in each case, the whole energy will be potential energy. The text-books suggest two alternative ways of considering the energy of the charge on a conductor. In the first place, one may imagine the charge q conveyed to the conductor piecemeal, in small elements δq_1, δq_2, ..., and one may evaluate the work in bringing these elements together against their mutual repulsion. The final energy stored up will be equal to the total work done. For a sphere of radius b this is found to be

$$\int_0^q \frac{q}{b}\, dq = \frac{q^2}{2b} \qquad \ldots\ldots(1).$$

Alternatively, when we have any conductor bearing a charge q, we may regard the energy as belonging to the electrostatic field and as residing in the medium outside the conductor, there being a certain density of energy in every element of volume—that of Faraday's tubes of force. The total energy is obtained by integrating over all space outside the conductor. If at any point of an electrostatic field the intensity is E, the density of energy at that point is $E^2/8\pi$ *in vacuo*. At a distance r from the centre of our spherical conductor the intensity E is by the inverse-square law equal to q/r^2. The volume of a spherical shell being $4\pi r^2 dr$, the energy in the whole of space outside the conductor is obtained by integrating from $r = b$ to $r = \infty$, which gives

$$\frac{1}{8\pi} \int_b^\infty \frac{q^2}{r^4} 4\pi r^2 dr = \frac{q^2}{2b} \qquad \ldots\ldots(2),$$

in agreement with the other method. The greater part of this energy lies in the region near the conductor where the field is most intense. If we draw round the conductor any larger sphere of radius r, the amount of energy in the medium outside this sphere will clearly be $q^2/2r$.

Now consider a medium of uniform dielectric constant K. Let there be in it a small spherical cavity of radius a, fig. 1, and within the cavity let us place our spherical conductor which has a slightly smaller radius b. Both arguments show that the energy of the charge will be smaller than it was for the same conductor *in vacuo*. From the first point of view, the work done in conveying elements of charge to the sphere will be less, because

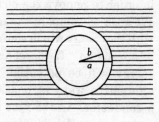

Fig. 1

the force of repulsion on the charge, while it is being brought through the dielectric, will be K times smaller than *in vacuo*. From the other point of view, for a given charge the energy in the surrounding medium will be less. Inside the cavity the intensity is the same as before, but in the dielectric the intensity E at a distance r from the centre will be now q/Kr^2; and the density of energy will be

$$\frac{KE^2}{8\pi} = \frac{q^2}{8\pi Kr^2} \qquad \ldots\ldots(3),$$

which is K times smaller than in a vacuum. We do not need to pay any attention to the empty part of the cavity between $r = b$ and $r = a$, since the energy here is quite unaltered by the presence of the dielectric. We need take into account only the energy in the region occupied by the dielectric. This, obtained by integrating (3) from $r=a$ to $r=\infty$, is

$$\frac{q^2}{2Ka}.$$

In a vacuum, as we have seen, the energy outside any sphere of radius a would be $q^2/2a$. Accordingly, we find that when the charge is in the dielectric its energy is *less* than when in a vacuum by an amount

$$\frac{q^2}{2a} - \frac{q^2}{2Ka} = \frac{q^2}{2a}\left(1 - \frac{1}{K}\right) \qquad \ldots\ldots(4).$$

In order to remove the charge from the dielectric into a vacuum this amount of work would have to be done. A calculation using the alternative method would, of course, lead to the same result. When K is large, the energy in the dielectric is almost completely annulled, in which case the value of (4) is nearly the same as $q^2/2a$.

In an atomic ion the positive or negative electric charge is not spread over the surface of a sphere, as in the conductor which we have been considering. But this does not matter, since the radius b of the conductor does not occur in (4); the charged body may equally well have a structure of its own. By inserting suitable values of q, a, and K, we can use (4) to obtain an estimate of the work required to move an ion from a solvent into a vacuum.* As to the charge q there is no doubt; for a singly charged ion we must insert the electronic charge ϵ, 4.7×10^{-10} electrostatic units, and so on. As for the size of the cavity, the solvent molecules are vibrating in contact with the ion; a large ion will occupy a bigger cavity than a small ion, and to obtain an estimate of the energy we may take the radius a to be 2×10^{-8} cm. or rather less. The values of K for a few solvents at

* The most convenient unit for measuring atomic energies is the electron-volt, i.e. the energy acquired by an electron or proton in falling through a potential difference of one volt; this is equal to 1.59×10^{-12} ergs. One electron-volt per molecule is equivalent to 23,050 calories per mol.

room temperature are given in the first part of Table I. It will
be seen that the values are so large that the factor $(1 - 1/K)$
differs little from unity.

Inserting the above values we find that for a positive or
negative singly charged ion the value of (4) is rather more than
3 electron-volts.

TABLE I

DIELECTRIC CONSTANTS AT ROOM TEMPERATURE

Liquids

	K	$(1 - 1/K)$
Ethyl alcohol	26	0·96
Methyl alcohol	34	0·97
Water	81	0·99

Solids

Rock salt	5·6	0·82
Potassium chloride	4·7	0·79

We have reached a result of fundamental importance. Our
estimate of (4) is certainly correct, although we have been using
throughout the language of the classical text-book, which is
artificial when applied to ions in a solvent. In reality the
dielectric consists of solvent molecules, among which the ion
is situated. Nevertheless the values which we have obtained
are certainly of the right order of magnitude. To remove a
positive or negative ion from a solvent to a vacuum a large
amount of work must be done. Conversely, if a free gaseous ion
enters a solvent, an equal amount of energy is liberated. This
is known as the *Solvation Energy*, and has a characteristic value
for each ion in each solvent.

From one point of view it is satisfactory that we have been
able to obtain a fair estimate of the solvation energies of singly
and multiply charged ions without attributing any structure to
the solvent. For this has drawn attention to the fundamental
nature of the solvation energy, and has shown how it arises
from the mere fact that any electrolytic ion is a charge situated
in a dielectric medium. It will be noticed further that not even
the radius of the ion occurs in (4). Consider, for example, a
proton introduced into a solvent. Although the radius ascribed

to the proton is many million times smaller than the radius of any ordinary ion like Li^+, this will have no bearing on the value of its solvation energy, since the latter depends only on the cavity among the solvent molecules where the proton is situated.

To give rise to the large difference in energy which we have found, there must be intense forces which oppose the removal of any charge from any dielectric. These forces are discussed in treatises on electrostatics. The image forces, which act on any charge held *in vacuo* near the surface of a uniform conducting body, are well known. In the same way, when a charge is held *in vacuo* near the surface of a uniform dielectric, it is attracted to the surface by an image force, which is more intense the nearer the surface. For a point charge q at a distance d from an infinite plane surface the value of the image force is $\dfrac{q^2}{4d^2}\dfrac{K-1}{K+1}$. Again, when the charge is situated within the dielectric near the surface, it is repelled from the surface farther into the dielectric; i.e. the force is in the same direction as before. When, therefore, a charge is taken from a dielectric into a vacuum, work has to be done against both these forces at the boundary. For a small charged sphere at distance not too near to the boundary, the formula for a point charge will apply. Plotting the work done against the perpendicular distance from the surface, we obtain a curve like fig. 2, where ABC is within the dielectric and CDE in the

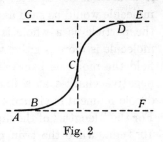

Fig. 2

vacuum. We see now the connection between this argument and the previous treatment. For the height EF on the diagram is just the total difference in energy, that is the solvation energy, which has been investigated in the preceding paragraphs.

Suppose now that a charge held at the point corresponding to E in fig. 2 is released. It will be accelerated into the dielectric, acquiring kinetic energy, equal at every point to the vertical distance between the curve $EDCA$ and the line EG, which represents the total energy. The charge will acquire energy equal to the height GA; in practice most of this energy will be at once dissipated as heat on collision with the molecules of the dielectric.

§ 2. SOLVENT MOLECULES

In the preceding section we have discussed the solvation energy from the point of view of classical electrostatics; the next step is to investigate, from the point of view of atomic physics, what is taking place. Why, when we bring a small charge towards the surface of a dielectric, does it experience a force of this magnitude? It has been found that liquid and gaseous dielectrics may be divided into two types; in one type each molecule has no permanent electric moment; in the other type the charge in the molecule is unevenly distributed, and each molecule behaves as a permanent electric dipole. In any molecule formed from two identical atoms, such as N_2, the distribution of charge is naturally exactly symmetrical about the centre of gravity. On the other hand, for molecules such as H_2O, HCl, and NH_3, where dissimilar positive charges are embedded in the common electron cloud, it would not be expected that the distribution of charge in the molecule would be such as to give zero electric moment. Though the particle as a whole is electrically neutral, one side of the molecule is more positive than the other, so that in an external field the molecule behaves as if it contained twin positive and negative charges at a fixed distance apart. The value of the dipole moment in electrostatic units will be of the order of 10^{-18}. For the "length" of the dipole will be of atomic dimensions, say 10^{-8} cm., while the twin positive and negative charges will be some fraction of the electronic charge, which is $4 \cdot 77 \times 10^{-10}$ e.s.u. The product will be of the order of 10^{-18}. The values in Table II are deduced from measurements of the dielectric constant of the vapour.

TABLE II

DIPOLE MOMENT OF MOLECULE

Water	$1 \cdot 8 \times 10^{-18}$ e.s.u.	Ammonia	$1 \cdot 5 \times 10^{-18}$ e.s.u.
Methyl alcohol	$1 \cdot 7$		
Ethyl alcohol	$1 \cdot 7$		

Every substance whose molecules are of this kind has a much larger dielectric constant than the other type, because when the substance is placed in any external electric field, its molecules tend to become oriented to some extent. Even in a field of some hundred thousand volts per centimetre this tendency to orientation is quite small at ordinary temperatures, owing to the thermal agitation. The field near a positive or negative ion, on the other hand, is much more intense than this. Let us, for example, calculate the intensity at a distance of 10 Ångstroms from a singly charged ion. We find

$$\frac{\epsilon}{r^2} = \frac{4\cdot77 \times 10^{-10}}{10^{-14}} = 4\cdot77 \times 10^4 \text{ e.s.u.}$$

When we remember that one e.s.u. of potential is equal to 300 volts, we see that the field has an intensity of about 14 million volts per cm. This is already much larger than any external field that we can apply to a dielectric; and at a point nearer to the ion, its field will be still more intense.

The most familiar solvents are liquids whose molecules are polar. We can thus see now roughly how the forces of attraction represented in fig. 2 arise. If a positive charge *in vacuo* is brought near the surface of a solvent, one or more of the nearest molecules will be swung round so as to point the negative ends of their dipole towards the charge, as shown in fig. 3. The positive ion is attracted by the negative ends of the dipoles, and is repelled by their positive ends. Since the former

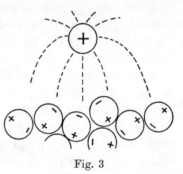

Fig. 3

are nearer, the ion experiences a resultant attraction towards the surface; a similar argument, of course, applies to a negative ion. This accounts for the curve of fig. 2. To calculate the exact form of this curve is at present an impossibly difficult problem, since one would have to take into account the mutual interaction of the solvent molecules and their thermal agitation. Fortunately, however, without taking into account any mechanism, we can estimate the total change in energy, represented by the vertical height EF in fig. 2. This must be given roughly by (4) for any positive or negative ion, whatever processes are involved. If an ion is allowed to enter a solvent, approximately this amount of energy is dissipated as the heat of solvation. Conversely, to liberate solvent molecules from the influence of an ion, work will always have to be done.

Consider now an ion in solution and moving about in the solvent with its normal Brownian movement. One or more of the solvent molecules in immediate contact with the ion may be attached to the ion and may accompany it. As the ion moves, however, a large number of other solvent molecules left behind in its wake are being removed from the field of its attraction, and work would have to be done, were not an equal number of similar molecules coming into its field in front. In fig. 4a an arbitrary sphere of influence has been drawn

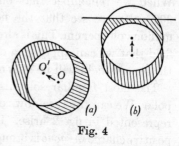

Fig. 4

round the ion for two positions of the ion O and O'. As the ion moves from O to O' one shaded area clearly becomes replaced by the other equal shaded area, and the potential energy of the ion is unaltered. This conception suggests a way of visualising the repulsion from the boundary which acts upon any charge within a dielectric—the repulsion which was mentioned above, and was represented by the portion ABC of the curve in fig. 2. Let the horizontal line in fig. 4b represent the dividing surface between a solvent of dielectric constant K and a medium of smaller dielectric constant K', which may, for example, be a vacuum. The ion approaching the boundary clearly does not acquire as much energy in front as it loses behind. Its potential energy rises; that is to say, it is repelled from the boundary.

§ 3. THE DISTRIBUTION OF THE ENERGY

Before passing on, it will be worth while to point out one aspect of solvation which will be useful later. It has been made clear that the solvation energy depends on the fact that in the dielectric the energy in the electrostatic field is reduced everywhere to $1/K$ of its value *in vacuo*. But the only intense part of the field is that immediately near the charge; and almost the whole of the energy is situated here. Consequently, if the field near the charge is reduced by the factor $1/K$, it matters little whether the more distant part of the field is reduced or not. In other words, if a charge is immediately surrounded by a mere shell of dielectric, the energy is almost the same as for an ion surrounded by a dielectric of infinite extent. This idea can easily be expressed quantitatively. The integral in (1) was taken from $r = a$ to $r =$ infinity. If instead we take it from $r = a$ to some larger radius $r = c$, we obtain for the solvation energy, instead of $q^2/2a \ (1 - 1/K)$, the expression

$$\frac{q^2}{2a} \left\{ 1 - \frac{1}{K} \left(1 - \frac{a}{c} \right) \right\} \qquad \ldots\ldots(5),$$

which reduces to the previous expression when c is large compared with a. And we see at once that if the thickness of the shell of the dielectric is equal to twice the diameter of the central cavity, that is, if $(c - a) = 4a$, the value of the solvation energy is already 80 per cent of the value for an infinite dielectric given by (5).

§ 4. IONIC CRYSTALS

Before leaving the subject of dielectrics, we may consider briefly the other class of substances of which examples are included in Table I, namely, those crystalline solids which when dissolved give rise to some of the most important conducting solutions with which this book is to deal. Since 1920 the idea has become familiar that we may regard many inorganic solid salts as consisting entirely of positive and negative ions held in a regular lattice by electrostatic forces—the arrangement being such that each ion has neighbours of opposite sign. In rock salt, for example, each positive ion is surrounded by six negatives, and each negative by six positives. If we fix attention on any particular ion we find that most of the electrostatic lines of force radiating from it, instead of extending out into space, come to an end upon the nearest neighbours of opposite sign. In fact, these nearest neighbours provide a little cavity for the ion, the field of the ion outside the cavity being mainly annulled.

It is not useful to consider the removal of a single positive or negative ion from the interior into a vacuum, as we did for a charge within a liquid. But we may imagine a whole piece of crystal pulled to pieces and broken up into its component ions. There is a theorem in electrostatics about the work required to break up any system of electric charges in this way, which will be mentioned later. Here we may notice that when the ions are all separated and distributed through space at long distances apart, the electrostatic field of each ion will possess its maximum energy. Clearly, in separating the ions, a large amount of work must have been done to supply this energy. In respect of each of those ions which in the crystal occupied a roughly spherical cavity of radius a_1 the energy supplied must have been

$$\frac{(m_1\epsilon)^2}{2a_1} \, (1 - 1/K),$$

where K is the dielectric constant of the original crystal and $m_1\epsilon$ is the charge on the ion. In respect of each of those ions, which in the crystal occupied a cavity equal in volume to a sphere of radius a_2, the work done must have been

$$\frac{(m_2\epsilon)^2}{2a_2} \, (1 - 1/K):$$

and so on, if there are more than two species of ion present. In this way we obtain a good estimate of the total amount of work required to split up the crystal into its ions, which is known as its Lattice Energy. In the case of ions in solution we were able to speak of the solvation energy of each positive and negative ion separately. In a crystal composed of two species of ions we shall express the lattice energy in electron-volts per ion pair. In a polyatomic substance the lattice energy is characteristic of the unit group of positive and negative ions from which the crystal is built up.

The work required to remove n pairs of ions from a dilute solution is n times the solvation energy of one pair. But it is worth noticing that the expressions which were given in the last paragraph for the energy which must be supplied in respect of an ion in a crystal are not the same as the work required to remove the ion from the lattice, leaving the other ions in situ. If we have any system of charges 1, 2, 3, ... in fixed positions, with purely coulomb forces between them, and if the work to remove the first charge to infinity, leaving the other charges in situ, is w_1, and the work required to remove the second charge to infinity when all the other charges, including the first, are present is w_2, and so on—then the work to break up the whole system of charges and leave them at rest at infinite distances from one another is

$$\tfrac{1}{2}\,(w_1 + w_2 + w_3 + \ldots) \qquad \ldots\ldots(6).$$

This result may be quickly verified in the case of two or three charges, and in text-books of electrostatics is proved for any number of charges. We shall make use of the theorem in a later chapter.

CHAPTER II

§ 1. ATOMIC IONS

The Bohr theory of quantised energy levels provided a model not only for atoms, but also for molecules, and for ions, atomic and molecular, positive and negative. In his papers published in 1913 Bohr himself applied the theory to atomic ions and to neutral molecules. The obvious extensions to molecular ions were made later.

The reader will be familiar with the idea of quantised excited states in any atom. The most loosely bound electron in the atom may be raised to any of a series of states of higher energy (corresponding in the Bohr theory to larger and larger orbits), until finally the electron becomes free, leaving behind a positive ion; the series of discrete levels has reached a limit at a certain energy equal to the ionisation potential of the atom. The process may be continued. The most loosely bound electron remaining behind in the positive ion may be raised to successively higher states—the excited levels of this ion—until this electron in turn becomes free, leaving behind a doubly charged positive ion. In this book we shall be less interested in the excited levels than in the energies of ionisation, $\mathscr{I}$, $\mathscr{I}_+$, etc., which are indicated in fig. 5.

The atoms of some elements are capable of taking up an additional electron to form an atomic negative ion. The normal state of such an ion has a quantised energy, and a definite amount of work is required to remove one electron and leave it at rest *in vacuo*. This, the ionisation potential of the negative ion, is quite similar to the ionisation potential of any atom or positive ion, and may be denoted by $\mathscr{I}_-$. An equal amount of energy is, of course, liberated when an electron at rest unites with an atom to form a negative ion. This amount of energy is sometimes known as the electron-affinity of the atom. It seems best, however, to speak of the ionisation potential of the negative ion, to bring it into line with the other ionisation potentials.

In fig. 5 is shown part of the scheme of levels for a single atom in various stages of ionisation. For completeness we have chosen an atom capable of forming a negative ion. Starting at the bottom of the diagram, a certain amount of work has to be done to remove the supernumerary electron, yielding a neutral atom. The removal of another electron by the expenditure of more work brings us up to the ground level of the singly charged ion, and so on. Each successive step requires more work than the one which preceded it. In the first place the extra electron in any

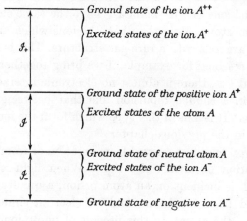

Fig. 5

negative ion is lightly bound, and the work required to detach it is always less than the work required to detach one from the same atom when neutral, for the latter means separating the electron from the positive core. The work required to separate a negative electron from a positive ion will naturally be still greater, and so on. Starting, for example, with the chlorine negative ion, Cl⁻, we see from Table XI on p. 201 that it takes 3·8 ϵ-volts for the first electron, 13 ϵ-volts for the second, 23 for the third, and so on. The known values for the light elements, determined from their line spectra, are assembled in this table. There are still many gaps in our knowledge, as will be seen; but values to within one ϵ-volt can often be estimated for any element from the known ionisation potentials of its neighbours in the table. Some of these values have been included in brackets.

This table illustrates some familiar features of ionic structure. If we look to see where the highest values occur in the table, we find that in the neighbourhood of sodium the highest values fall on a diagonal, and belong to Ne, Na^+, Mg^{++} and Al^{+++}. All ions lying on such a diagonal have the same number of electrons. Not only Na^+, Mg^{++} and Al^{+++}, but also the fluorine negative ion F^- have the same electronic configuration as the neon atom. Similarly the ions Cl^-, K^+ and Ca^{++} have the same closed shells as the argon atom. More than half the ions which are familiar in solution are ions with a rare-gas structure. This is important for several reasons; for example, if we bring together two ions, like K^+ and Cl^-, there is almost no electronic interaction until there sets in a sudden repulsion like that between two inert argon atoms. It is ions of this type which form the ionic lattices mentioned in the previous chapter.

An electron may be removed from an atom or from an ion by the absorption of ultra-violet light. When light of suitable wave-length is incident on an atom or ion, a quantum $h\nu$ may be removed from the beam, and an electron simultaneously ejected from the atom. In this process of photo-ionisation the frequency of the incident light must be at least as great as ν_0, given by

$$h\nu_0 = \mathscr{I} \qquad\qquad \ldots\ldots(7).$$

Any wave-length on the high frequency side of ν_0 may be operative; hence in the absorption spectrum we have a continuous absorption band starting at a frequency ν_0, characteristic of the atom or ion in question. In the case of many negative ions, the ionisation potential is so small that the absorption band would be found to begin in the visible region of the spectrum, if the band could be observed. In practice we cannot obtain a sufficiently high concentration of these negative ions in any gas to locate this absorption.

The removal of an electron from an atom or ion may be

pictured most easily by means of a potential energy diagram. Let us take first the hydrogen atom, and consider the potential energy of the electron along any straight line drawn through the proton; it will be simply $-\epsilon^2/r$. With increasing distance r the attraction falls off, and the curve on either side becomes asymptotic to a horizontal line, fig. 6a. Any horizontal line above this one represents the energy of a free electron. If such an electron is captured by the proton to form a hydrogen atom, it will settle down eventually in its

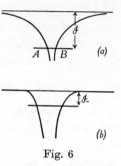

Fig. 6

lowest quantised level, which may be represented on the diagram by a line AB at a depth of 13·53 ϵ-volts (this being the ionisation potential of a hydrogen atom).

It is only for the hydrogen atom itself that the potential energy curve is exactly $-\epsilon^2/r$. For other atoms the curve will resemble fig. 6a, but will differ from $-\epsilon^2/r$ to some extent, owing to the presence of the other electrons.

If we wish to consider the removal of an electron from a singly charged helium ion, He$^+$, the appropriate potential energy curve will be of course exactly $-2\epsilon^2/r$. For other singly charged positive ions the curve will differ from this to some extent for small r.

If we wish to represent in this way the removal of the supernumerary electron from a singly charged negative ion, we need to know its potential energy in the field of the neutral atom. In this case the force of attraction falls off much more suddenly after a certain radius. The curve, instead of tending to the horizontal, as $1/r$, will become horizontal more suddenly as in fig. 6b. Owing to the peculiar form of this field, few, if any, atomic negative ions will possess excited levels. They will show no line absorption spectrum, but only a continuous absorption, due to ejection of the electron. This restriction does not apply to molecular negative ions.

In the case of atoms and atomic ions the absorption which gives rise to excitation always takes the form of a line spectrum;

for most polyatomic molecules it consists of wide bands which cannot be resolved into lines; for diatomic gases the absorption spectrum can usually be resolved into lines, except when the gas is at high pressure; then the lines always become blurred and tend to form continuous bands of absorption.

§ 2. MOLECULES AND MOLECULAR IONS

If we remove an electron from an atom, we obtain a positive atomic ion. On the other hand, when we remove an electron from a molecule, in many cases we do not obtain a molecular positive ion, because the molecule immediately dissociates into its constituent atoms. If one valence electron is removed from a molecule, the bonding action of the remaining valence electrons is sometimes sufficient to maintain a stable positive ion, but for many molecular species it is not. As a result, whereas the spectra of many atomic ions are well known, the spectra of molecular positive ions have been studied in a few cases only, namely, N_2^+, O_2^+, $(CO)^+$, $(HCl)^+$, and certain hydrides, such as $(ZnH)^+$. For some molecular species not only ionisation but even excitation causes the molecule to dissociate. For example, if an electron in the NaBr molecule is raised to an excited state, the bonding is so weak that the molecule may immediately dissociate into two neutral atoms.

Although their spectra have not been observed, the existence of polyatomic positive and negative ions has been known for a very long time. When the mobility of ions in gases was first studied, it was found that both positive and negative ions often united with molecules to form polyatomic ions of lower mobility. It has since been shown that this combination is mainly with molecules of water vapour and other impurities present in the gas.

A molecule or molecular ion is stable because it requires a certain amount of work to separate the nuclei. If we begin to separate a diatonic molecule into two neutral atoms, the attraction between the atoms decreases very rapidly, as the distance between the nuclei increases. Since the development of quantum mechanics we understand that the attraction between two neutral particles is due to the fact that, when two atoms are brought together, one or more electrons begin to circulate round both the nuclei; the resultant forces of attraction are usually known as "exchange forces". In the case of any diatomic molecule or molecular ion, we may plot the potential energy against the distance apart of the two nuclei, and obtain a curve like the portion *CDE* of fig. 2, becoming horizontal as the attraction falls to zero. On the other hand, if we push the two nuclei nearer together, there is an intense repulsion between them. The curve rises again steeply, as *FG* in fig. 7. For the simplest molecules and molecular ions quantum mechanics enables us to calculate the shape of this curve. For other molecules we

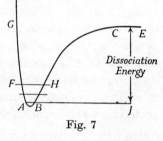

Fig. 7

have empirical curves, whose constants have been deduced from the characteristic spectra. The interpretation of such a curve according to classical mechanics was as follows. To represent the constant energy of the system, we must draw a horizontal line on the diagram. The vertical distance between this line and the potential energy curve represents kinetic energy. If the horizontal line cuts the curve twice, as *FH*, this kinetic energy is kinetic energy of molecular vibration. The distance d between the nuclei oscillates continually between two extreme values, such as *F* and *H*, depending upon the total energy U of the system. The greater the energy, the wider the amplitude of vibration, until at a certain energy the atoms will fly apart. This, of course, can occur when the horizontal line representing U lies above the horizontal portion *CE* of the curve.

The application of the Bohr principle of quantisation to this vibration will mean that only certain values of U are allowed, giving a set of discrete levels. At low temperature nearly all the molecules will be in the lowest level of the set, below which no energy is allowed. The work required to separate the atoms completely from this initial level, AB, and to leave them at rest is known as the dissociation energy of the molecule. It is evidently equal to the vertical distance JE in fig. 7.

The number of molecules in a gas at temperature T which possess a certain amount of vibrational energy E will, by the Boltzmann Law, be proportional to $e^{-E/kT}$. This fraction is independent of the volume in which the gas is confined. To find the number of molecules in a gas at temperature T which are dissociated into atoms, one cannot simply insert the dissociation energy into the Boltzmann factor, since the equilibrium will depend on the volume in which the gas is contained. At equilibrium the number of atoms recombining per second is equal to the number of molecules dissociating. Recombination results only from an encounter between two atoms, and the frequency of encounters depends on the pressure of the gas. For diatomic molecules behaving as a perfect gas, and possessing a dissociation energy D, the fraction α of the total number dissociated into atoms is given by*

$$\frac{\alpha^2}{(1-\alpha)\,v} = A e^{-D/kT} \qquad \ldots\ldots(8),$$

where v is the volume, and factor A is a function of temperature depending on the masses of the atoms. If we compare various gases at the same temperature and pressure, those with a high value of D will be much less dissociated than those with a low value of D. If we consider a particular gas at a given temperature, the right-hand side of (8) is constant; any change in v is accompanied by a change in α. If we increase the volume, α will increase and tend towards unity. For any gas we can in theory make the dissociation approach 100 per cent., even at room temperature, though for a gas with a large value of D the requisite pressures are extremely low. In practice hardly any of the common gases give an appreciable amount of dissociation at room temperature, because the required pressures are too low.

* Fowler, *Statistical Mechanics*, Chapter v.

We have been speaking so far of the dissociation of a molecule into neutral atoms. We shall be interested also in the dissociation of a polyatomic ion into an atomic ion and a neutral molecule, for which again a characteristic amount of energy will be required. In speaking of the dissociation energy of a molecule or molecular ion, we ought always to specify the particles into which it is being split; but this is usually clear from the context.

When an electron in a molecule is raised to an excited level, the bonding between the atoms is generally different from when it was in its ground state.

The equilibrium distance between the nuclei may be altered, and the work required to dissociate the molecule may be less. In fact, the potential energy curve, fig. 7, may have quite a different shape from that characteristic of the unexcited molecule. Further, an ionised molecule will have a different curve from the same molecule when neutral. As a result of this, we need to define carefully what we mean by the ionisation potential of any molecule or molecular ion.

Let $ABCE$ be the curve for any neutral diatomic molecule, AB being the lowest vibration level. When the distance between the nuclei is large, that is, at E, we have two separate atoms. Let us ionise one of these atoms, removing the electron to infinity. The energy of the system has been increased by an amount equal to the work we have done, namely the ionisation potential $\mathscr{I}$ of this atom. In fig. 8 let the vertical distance EL be $\mathscr{I}$. Now let us bring together the ion and the atom. If they form a stable positive molecular ion, we shall obtain a curve

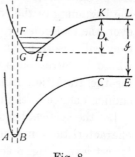

Fig. 8

such as $LKJHGF$, possessing a set of vibration levels; let GH be the lowest of the set; then the vertical height of KL above GH is D_+, the dissociation potential of the molecular ion.

By the ionisation potential of any neutral molecule we mean the work required to remove a valence electron and leave the resulting positive molecular ion in a specified state; but in what state? When an electron is ejected from a molecule, it leaves the molecule in an interval less than 10^{-14} sec. Compared with this, the period of vibration of the atoms along their line of centres is long—more than 10^{-13} sec. As a result, when the molecule is ionised, the separation of the nuclei scarcely changes during the actual escape of the electron. Or rather we should say that a transition implying a sudden change in the nuclear separation is relatively improbable; this is known as the Franck-Condon principle. Now a transition with unaltered nuclear separation means, on fig. 8, a transition with unaltered value of the abscissa. Vertical dotted lines have, therefore, been drawn in fig. 8 through A and B.

If the molecule is initially in its lowest level AB, the least energy necessary to ionise it is that given by the vertical height of GH above AB. If we draw up a list for various molecules, it is this quantity which we shall tabulate as the characteristic ionisation potential. It is this quantity which determines the minimum energy that impinging electrons must have to eject an electron, and determines the minimum frequency that incident light must have to produce photo-ionisation, i.e. it fixes the beginning of the continuous absorption spectrum. If, however, the molecules are illuminated with a continuous spectrum, they will absorb much more heavily those shorter wave lengths whose $h\nu$ corresponds more nearly to the height FB on fig. 8; for the transition from AB to FJ can take place without a sudden change in the nuclear separation.

Let the vertical height of GH above AB be denoted by $\mathscr{J}$, the characteristic ionisation potential of the molecule from its lowest level. Fig. 8 shows clearly a relation between $\mathscr{I}$, $\mathscr{J}$, D and D_+. Since the vertical height of CE above AB is equal to D, the total height of KL above AB is equal to $(\mathscr{I}+D)$; but this is also equal to $(\mathscr{J}+D_+)$. We have then for any molecule

$$\mathscr{J} + D_+ = \mathscr{I} + D \qquad \ldots\ldots(9).$$

Let us consider in greater detail the formation of a diatomic ion from an atomic ion and a neutral atom. If the structure of the ion is spherically symmetrical, and that of the atom the same, there is a unique potential energy curve like $FGKL$ of fig. 8. On the other hand, if either particle has a non-spherical structure, the potential energy will depend on the relative orientation of the atomic axes. Since every system tends to go into its state of lowest potential energy, the atoms will take up the optimum orientation which leads to a curve $FGKL$ with the deepest minimum. This is the only curve in which we are interested.

A similar consideration applies to the formation of a triatomic ion from an atomic ion and a diatomic molecule (or from a neutral atom and a diatomic ion). There will be a particular configuration of the triatomic ion which has a lower potential energy than any other. The particles will spontaneously take up the configuration which possesses the deepest minimum, and we are not concerned with any other curve. If the molecule in question is a polar molecule, we can guess at once what is the optimum orientation. If we are bringing up a positive ion, the lowest potential energy will be when the negative side of the dipole is directed towards the ion. If we are bringing up a negative ion, the lowest potential energy will be when the positive side of the dipole is directed towards it. If the molecule is free to rotate, the particles will easily take up their optimum configuration.

We should expect that polar molecules would show a marked tendency to form polyatomic ions in the way just described, when atomic ions are available. Powell and Brata* found evidence of such formation in studying the movement of positive ions through non-polar gases containing a small number of polar molecules as impurity. Thus sodium positive ions passing through nitrogen apparently attached themselves to ammonia molecules present as impurity, to form polyatomic ions $(Na.NH_3)^+$ as well as $(Na.N_2H_6)^+$; and in passing through hydrogen that had not been completely dried, the Na^+ ions appeared to combine with water molecules to form $(Na.H_2O)^+$.

* *Proc. Roy. Soc.* A, **138**, 129 (1932).

Although we do not know the properties of such an ion in detail, there is no doubt that, if we could plot the potential energy against the distance between the sodium nucleus and the oxygen nucleus in the H_2O molecule, we should obtain a curve of the usual molecular type; at a certain distance the attraction changes over into the familiar intense repulsion. To remove the Na^+ ion from such a complex requires a definite amount of work; the dissociation energy of the molecular ion corresponds to the depth of the minimum of the potential energy. There is no doubt that the negative polyatomic ions which are found in mobility experiments are formed in the same way, though these have never been studied in detail.

It should be noted that these molecules, H_2O and NH_3, possess the same number of electrons as the neon atom. This fact is important, not only in the formation of polyatomic ions, but also when water and liquid ammonia are acting as solvents. An ion like $(Na.H_2O)^+$ presumably consists of closed electronic shells in contact. For this reason the Na^+ retains its identity, not only in this polyatomic ion, but also when dissolved in water or other solvent whose molecules are similar.

From the clustering which is found in these experiments it is known that an atomic ion in a gas can attach several molecules to itself. To make clear the nature of such a cluster, let us carry out an imaginary experiment *in vacuo* with a particular ion and a small number of polar molecules (not more than six). Starting with the polar molecules equidistant from the ion, fig. 9a, we bring them towards the ion from different directions, keeping them equidistant from the ion all the time. If we plot in the usual way the potential energy of the system against the mutual distance d, we obtain a definite curve, which falls owing to the attraction. At a certain small value of d, when the polar

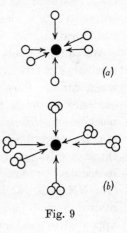

(a)

(b)

Fig. 9

molecules are close, the attraction will certainly change over to
an intense repulsion, and the curve will rise again rapidly. The
system is not essentially different from the simpler molecular
ion described in the preceding paragraph. The curve again has
the same shape as for a diatomic molecule, fig. 7. The minimum
will, of course, be deeper than when only a single polar molecule
is present.

Instead of starting with six separate polar molecules, we may
start with six groups of polar molecules, enough to form an
envelope round the ion two or three molecules thick. Bringing
them together as in fig. 9 b, we shall obtain a potential energy
curve of the same type, but with a minimum somewhat deeper
still, due to the additional contributions by the outer polar
molecules. Each of these outer molecules, being situated in a
weaker part of the electrostatic field, makes a smaller contribution to the energy than the innermost molecules, which are in
the most intense part of the field (compare § 3 of Chapter I).
If we go on now to add large numbers of additional polar molecules, the minimum of the potential energy curve becomes only a
little deeper, and its depth tends to a definite limit. We thus reach
the conclusion to which the whole of this argument has been
leading, namely that if the polar molecules which we are using
are molecules of water or other solvent,
and if we pack a sufficient number of
them round the ion, the resulting aggre-
gate is no longer to be regarded as a
molecular ion, such as $(Na.nH_2O)^+$,
but as a Na^+ ion in the middle of a
minute drop of liquid. And the depth
of the minimum of the potential energy
curve, fig. 10, is now just the solvation

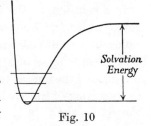

Fig. 10

energy of the ion in this liquid. For the energy of its electrostatic
field has been cut down from the value *in vacuo* to the value
characteristic of this particular solvent.

In this way we are able to obtain a link with molecular
physics. The electrolytic ion has all the properties of a poly-

atomic ion, with the solvation energy taking the place of the dissociation energy. In the potential valley of fig. 10 there will be a set of allowed levels, and the ion cannot have energy less than the lowest of these. In any solution we can visualise each solvated ion as vibrating to and fro near the bottom of a deep potential valley of its own. At room temperature most will be in their lowest level, but a few will possess more vibrational energy than the rest, in accordance with the Boltzmann Law.

We have now discussed ions in solution from three points of view: (1) as charges moving in a continuous medium of dielectric constant K; (2) as charges moving in a liquid consisting of molecular dipoles; and (3) as atomic and molecular ions combining with molecules of the solvent to form polyatomic molecular ions, which will possess characteristic energy levels and a characteristic absorption spectrum. Each of these points of view will play a part in the following chapters. It must not be thought that, because (3) gives the most detailed picture, (1) and (2) are to be discarded. On the contrary, it is important to bear in mind that the solvation energy is of a very general nature. As shown in Chapter I, its magnitude can be estimated from the idea of a continuous dielectric medium—a fact which should continually remind us of its fundamental nature, even when dealing with the polyatomic ions.

In a solution, as the ions move about, the solvent molecules come under the influence of the ions. But if we consider a sufficiently dilute solution at any moment, we find that most of the solvent molecules are not appreciably affected by the presence of the ions at that moment. We can regard the solution as consisting of solvated ions moving about in pure solvent. On the other hand, in a more concentrated solution, where the amount of unmodified solvent is no longer large, the situation is much more complicated. Since any theoretical study must proceed from the simple to the complex, we shall be concerned in this volume with dilute solutions only.

CHAPTER III

§ 1. THE LATTICE ENERGY OF IONIC CRYSTALS

Although a few of the important electrolytic solutions are obtained by dissolving gases, such as HCl, the majority are obtained by dissolving crystalline solids, of a type which are electrical insulators. On the other hand, a large part of our information about electrolytic ions is obtained by dipping metallic electrodes into the solution. In order to understand the processes involved, it is necessary to be familiar with modern ideas as to the structure of crystals, both insulators and conductors. In this chapter, therefore, we shall review some of their most important properties.

An ionic crystal such as rock-salt is an insulator at room temperature. Before the introduction of quantum mechanics one would have said that this was because the crystal is built up of positive and negative ions which cannot change places, and because each valence electron is permanently attached to a negative ion, from which it cannot move. Although quantum mechanics gives a different description of the insulating properties, the final result is much the same as before; the electrons may change places, but in doing so they spend so little time in the neighbourhood of the metallic cores that the latter may still be regarded as positive ions bearing a charge almost equal to ϵ. In the rock-salt structure each positive ion has as nearest neighbours six negative ions, and each negative ion has likewise as nearest neighbours six positive ions. The electrostatic attraction between these neighbours of opposite sign is, of course, stronger than the electrostatic repulsion between the more distant ions of like sign, with the result that the ions of the crystals are bound together.

An estimate of the lattice energy of such a crystal was obtained in § 4 of Chapter I. The idea of calculating lattice energies was first developed by Born and Landé in 1918 by an

entirely different method. We know that if we wish to compress
a crystal, we meet with an intense repulsion and have to do
work. If, on the other hand, we wish to stretch the crystal,
we again have to do work. It is clear then that if the potential
energy of the crystal at room temperature is plotted against its
volume, the curve will resemble fig. 7. The minimum in the
curve will occur at that volume which is the normal volume of
the crystal at room temperature.

We may imagine the crystal to be stretched or compressed
uniformly in all directions—that is, in such a way that each
interatomic distance changes in the same proportion. Instead
of plotting the energy of the crystal against its volume, we may
plot it against the interatomic distance r. We again obtain a
curve with a minimum, like curve ABG of fig. 11. The minimum
occurs at that value of r which is the normal lattice spacing at
room temperature.

Born and Landé suggested that for crystals where both positive and negative ions have the closed electronic shells of the
rare-gas structure, this curve could be
calculated by regarding it as the sum
of two simple curves CD and EFG,
fig. 11. If we add the ordinates of the
two dotted curves CD and EFG, we
obtain the full curve ABG. CD represents the repulsion between neighbours
which sets in when the electronic shells
come into contact. EFG represents the
simple electrostatic between all ions of
opposite sign *minus* the electrostatic
repulsion between all ions of the same

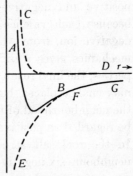

Fig. 11

sign. As already noticed, there is a net attraction, because
nearest neighbours are of opposite sign. The minimum of the
curve AB occurs at that value of r for which this electrostatic
attraction happens to be balanced by the non-electrostatic repulsion between ions in contact. In fig. 11 we are supposing the
interatomic distance to change uniformly in all directions, so

that the unit cell of the lattice changes in size but not in shape, the geometric configuration of the ions remaining the same throughout. Since the electrostatic forces both of attraction and repulsion vary as $1/r^2$, the resultant attraction varies as $1/r^2$, and the potential energy as $1/r$. Consequently the ordinates of the curve EFG are proportional to $1/r$, like those of the curve in fig. 6a.

The lattice energy of the crystal is the total work one has to do to separate the ions to large distances from each other. There are two ways in which we may suppose this to be done. Taking the ions off the surface of the crystal, we may remove them one by one to infinity. Alternatively, we may, using fig. 11, imagine the lattice-spacing to be increased uniformly in all directions, so that the lattice preserves its arrangement even when the ions are sufficiently far from each other. The same amount of work must, of course, be done in either case. The total work that we have to do is clearly equal to the depth of the minimum of the curve in fig. 11; this, then, is equal to the lattice energy.

We may notice that the minimum lies very little above the electrostatic curve EF (because the curve CD rises so steeply from a value near zero). From this fact, that the lattice energy is mainly electrostatic, we can draw conclusions about the lattice energies of different crystals of the same type. Suppose that fig. 11 gives the curve for a particular substance, say NaCl, and consider what will be the shape of the curve for a substance like KBr or RbI, which has the same crystal structure, but is built up of *larger* ions. The minimum will occur at a larger value of r, that is, farther to the right in fig. 11. Consequently the minimum will be shallower, for it must lie above the electrostatic curve EF. As shown in Table XII a crystal composed of pairs of large ions has a smaller lattice energy than one of the same structure composed of small ions.

Let us return now to the uniform expansion of any lattice. For the sake of a discussion to be given in a later chapter it will be convenient to consider here the intermediate stages in this expansion of the lattice. When a separation corresponding to the point G in fig. 11 has been reached, the interatomic distance is already four times the initial lattice spacing; work equal to the height DG has still to be done to complete the expansion; we know that this is rather more than 1/4 of the total lattice energy, since the ordinates of the curve EFG are proportional to $1/r$. Similarly, when the volume occupied by the extended crystal is 1000 times the normal value, the work still to be done will be rather more than 1/10th of the lattice energy. This subject will be taken up again in Chapter VII in a discussion of ions in solutions. Here we shall pass on to the study of metals.

§ 2. METALS

Pieces of metal have usually a micro-crystalline structure; that is to say, they consist of aggregates of crystals of extremely small dimensions packed together with random orientations. Whereas large single crystals of metallic salts have always been familiar objects, it is only since 1920 that much progress has been made in methods of growing large single crystals of various metals. In discussing any piece of metal, we shall not need to distinguish between one surface and another, for in every surface all possible crystal faces will be many times represented. The structure is, however, everywhere crystalline. It consists of positive atomic cores arranged in a regular lattice, while the valence electrons move freely among them.

Let us first consider a piece of metal which is electrically neutral. For brevity it is convenient to take a monovalent metal, like silver, where the positive core bears only a single charge ϵ. If we fix attention on a particular positive core, either in the interior or on the surface of the lattice, its positive charge is on the average neutralised by an equal negative charge. This negative charge is not the charge of any particular electron but is contributed by all the moving electrons which pass by.

When an insulated metallic conductor bears a negative charge, it means that the total number of electrons in the conductor is greater than the number required to neutralise the atomic positive cores which form the metal lattice. The electric charge lies in the surface layer, but the electrons which are present in excess do not remain attached to any particular atoms. Similarly, if an insulated piece of metal bears a positive charge, it is because the total number of electrons in the conductor is smaller than the number required to neutralise all the positive cores of the lattice. But again it is not any particular surface ions of the lattice which remain unneutralised. Suppose, for example, that, starting with a piece of metal which is electrically neutral, we deposit on the surface a small number n of additional positive cores of the same element, each bearing a charge ϵ. When the positive cores have taken up their places on the surface of the lattice, they participate fully in the free electrons of the metal on an equal footing with the other positive cores. The piece of metal as a whole now bears a charge $n\epsilon$, which is distributed over its surface and no longer has any connection with the particular atomic cores which brought it to the metal.

We can now begin to discuss the work required to split up any metallic crystal into its constituents. We have pointed out that if we fix our attention on a particular positive core of the lattice, there is no particular valence electron belonging to this core. Nevertheless if we detach one of the positive cores from the surface, one of the valence electrons usually comes away with it; that is to say, we remove a neutral atom. The evaporation of liquid mercury in the form of neutral atoms is perhaps more familiar than that of solid metals. To detach a neutral atom from any metal, we have to do a certain amount of work against the forces of attraction which hold the atom in its place. This work has a characteristic value for each metal, and is known as the Sublimation Energy.

On the other hand, we may imagine ourselves to be detaching a positive core from the surface of a metal without at the same time bringing away a valence electron with it; i.e. a negative charge remains behind on the metal, and we obtain a free positive ion. When a positive core is being removed in this way, the forces of attraction will be of different intensity from the previous case where the core was accompanied by an electron, and the total work will be greater. Each metal will, therefore, possess a

second characteristic quantity—the work required to detach a
positive core, which we shall denote by the letter Y. This
quantity is of more interest than the sublimation energy and
we shall pay more attention to it.

Consider a positive core vibrating to and fro in its place on
the surface of a metal, and suppose a straight line drawn perpendicular to the surface at this point. Consider how the
potential energy will depend on the position of the positive core
on this line. On the one hand, going away from the surface, the
forces of attraction fall off rapidly, so that the curve soon becomes horizontal. On the other hand, if we attempt to push the
atomic core inwards into the crystal from its position of equilibrium on the surface, we meet, of course, with
an intense repulsion. The curve is, consequently,
of the same shape as fig. 7 for a diatomic molecule. On the surface of a metal at room temperature each positive core is vibrating near the
bottom of a potential valley, fig. 12. The depth
of the valley is the work required to remove

Fig. 12

the particle from its lowest vibrational level. Thus the dissociation energy of fig. 7 is replaced by the quantity Y if we are
removing a positive ion from a metal surface.

Conversely, if we bring a positive core up to the metal, the
potential energy will follow a curve like fig. 12 from right to left.
If the core settles down on the surface in its lowest vibration
level, we receive an amount of energy equal to Y.

For the removal of a neutral atom from a metal or its deposition on the surface, we shall have a curve similar to fig. 12;
except that the depth of the potential valley is the sublimation
energy S, instead of Y. In order to escape from the metal a
surface atom in its lowest vibration level must acquire energy
greater than S. All solid metals have so large a value of S that
they exert only a very small vapour pressure at room temperature. For every metal the value of Y is still greater than that
of S. The relation between these two quantities will be determined in Chapter XIV.

§ 3. ELECTRONS IN METALS

We shall turn next to the behaviour of the valence electrons in metals. The electrical image force which arises between any charge and a metal surface has already been mentioned in Chapter I. If a piece of metal bearing *no* charge of electricity has been placed in a vacuum, and an electron is brought towards the surface and taken into the metal, the potential energy of the electron will be given by a curve similar to *EDCBA* of fig. 2. If we consider an electron taken through a slab of metal and out the other side, its potential energy will rise again at the other surface, the whole curve being a "potential box" like fig. 13a.

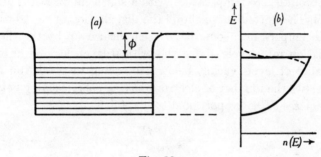

Fig. 13

The depth of this box varies from about 6 ε-volts for the alkali metals to nearly 20 ε-volts for metals of high valency. If at ordinary low temperatures the free electrons possessed only small kinetic energies, of the order of kT as expected from classical theory, we should have to picture them in energy levels near the bottom of the box; and the work required to remove an electron from the metal would be from 6 to 20 ε-volts for the various elements. Both experiment and quantum theory, however, agree that most of the free electrons in any metal have much higher kinetic energies, even at absolute zero temperature, the energies of comparatively few of the valence electrons being near the bottom of the box. The majority of the electrons cannot fall down into these low energy levels, because by the Exclusion

Principle each level can accommodate a strictly limited number
of electrons. We have then a wide band of electrons filling about
two-thirds of the potential box, as in fig. 13. At absolute zero
temperature there is at the top of this band a sharp division
between levels which are completely full, and levels above, which
are completely empty; the highest occupied level is known as
the critical level of the metal; below this level there are no
vacant levels, for, if there were, electrons would immediately
fall down into them.

In fig. 13b the ordinates correspond exactly to those of
fig. 13a, while abscissae give the number of electrons per unit
energy range. The full curve shows the distribution of electrons
at absolute zero temperature, with a sharp cut off at the critical
level. The dotted curve shows the distribution of electrons at a
high temperature; some have been thrown up by the thermal
agitation into levels above the critical level, leaving an equal
number of levels vacant below. According to the Fermi-Dirac
statistics the number of electrons having energies lying between
E and $E + dE$ is proportional to

$$\frac{\sqrt{E}\,dE}{e^{(E-E_0)/kT} + 1} \qquad \ldots\ldots(10),$$

where E_0 is the energy of the critical level. Upwards from the
critical level the number of electrons falls off at a rate nearly
the same as that given by the usual Boltzmann factor. This
decrease is so rapid that if the curve for room temperature were
drawn on the diagram, it would be indistinguishable from the
curve for absolute zero temperature. It is not any particular
electrons which inhabit the high levels above the critical level,
but there is a continual interchange; through collisions a certain
population of electrons with high energy is maintained, just as
among molecules in the kinetic theory of gases.

The work required to remove an electron from the critical
level of a metal and to leave it at rest in a vacuum is known as
the electronic work function of the metal, and will be denoted
by ϕ. For each metal ϕ has a characteristic value, varying from

about 2 ϵ-volts for the alkali metals to more than 6 ϵ-volts for platinum. For most metals the value of ϕ lies between 3 and 5·5 ϵ-volts. If, instead of removing an electron from the critical level, we remove one from a lower level, an electron will immediately fall down into this vacant level; the final state of the metal will be the same as before, namely with a vacancy at the critical level.

Suppose now that an electron is placed at rest in a vacuum near the surface of a piece of metal whose temperature is near the absolute zero. The electron will be drawn by the electrical image forces into the metal, where it will have a kinetic energy greater than the electrons resident in the metal. By collision energy will be lost and the electron will fall to a lower level. It cannot fall to a level lower than the critical level, because the lower levels are already full. The electron will accordingly settle down at the critical level, and the total energy that has been liberated is equal to ϕ, the work-function of the metal. The same will be true if the metal is at room temperature; although there are now some vacant levels below the critical level, the thermal agitation must keep a definite fraction of these empty, and again the energy liberated is ϕ.

§ 4. CONTACT POTENTIAL DIFFERENCE

From the values given in Table XIV it will be seen that the electronic work functions of the various elements range from 2 to more than 6 ϵ-volts. Consider what will happen when pieces of two different metals are brought near together. For this purpose we need to know the potential energy of an electron along a line drawn through the two pieces of metal. The required curve is obtained by joining together two curves like fig. 13 a, one with a smaller work-function than the other; the initial condition is thus given by curve a of fig. 14. It will be convenient to suppose first that the pieces of metal are at very low temperature, so that there is a clear demarcation between the electronic levels which are completely full and those above which are completely empty.

According to classical mechanics electrons cannot pass from

one potential box to the other unless they are given sufficient energy to enable them to pass over the intervening potential barrier with positive kinetic energy. Quantum mechanics, on the other hand, allows them to pass through the intervening region, where their kinetic energy would be negative. When the gap is small, an electron can pass from one metal into any vacant level of equal energy in the other metal. The electrons are, of course, unable to pass to levels of higher energy, since energy must be conserved.

Consider then what will happen when the two pieces of metal of fig. 14 are brought near together. As soon as the distance between the metal surfaces falls below about 15 Ångstrom units electrons begin to stream from A to the vacant levels in B. This is not balanced by a similar stream from B to A, since there are no vacant levels in A of the same energy as the occupied levels in B. Owing to this transfer of electrons the surface of A gradually becomes positively charged and the adjacent surface of B negatively charged, owing to which an

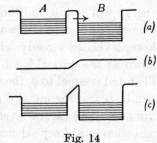

Fig. 14

electrostatic field grows up in the space between these charged surfaces. As soon as this field appears, the curve a of fig. 14 no longer represents the potential energy of an electron along a line through the metals, for the potential energy of an electron in this field must be superposed on the initial energy. In the gap between A and B the curve must now be sloping instead of horizontal. The ordinates of a curve like curve b must be added to the ordinates of curve a. The escape of electrons from A to B will clearly go on until this slope is sufficiently large to bring the top of the occupied levels of A opposite to the top of the occupied levels of B, as in curve c of fig. 14. The flow of electrons into B is then automatically stopped and the whole will be in equilibrium.

In the preceding paragraph we supposed the pieces of metal

to be at very low temperature. At room temperature the distribution of the electrons is so nearly the same, that a separate discussion will scarcely be necessary. Passage of electrons from A to B and from B to A are both possible at first, but the former is enormously predominant until the condition of fig. 14c is brought about by the growth of the electric field in the gap. Then the number of electrons passing in each second from B to A is equal to the number passing from A to B.

We should expect then that when we put into contact pieces of two metals whose work-functions are different, the metal with the larger work-function would become negatively charged with respect to the other. In fact, we should be able to obtain a series, if we arranged all the metals in the order of the values of their work-functions. This is the explanation given in 1906 by Einstein* for the well-known contact potential difference between metals. The metals can be arranged in a series such that on contact each member in the series becomes negatively charged with respect to the member preceding it.

The electrons which escape from A do not spread through B to any large extent, because the positive charge left on A holds them on the adjacent surface of B by its attraction. The two charged surfaces, in fact, form an electrical double layer. It is evident from fig. 14a that the strength of the double layer which gives equilibrium is equal to the difference between the two electronic work-functions, $(\phi_A - \phi_B)$, for when the potential difference has this value, the critical level of one metal is brought opposite the critical level of the other. Thus, when a piece of platinum is put into contact with a piece of alkali metal the contact potential difference will amount to about 4 volts.

Contact potential differences are additive. If the metals A and B are put into electrical connection, not by direct contact but by inserting a third metal C between them, the potential difference between A and B is the same as before. This clearly must be so, since

$$(\phi_A - \phi_C) + (\phi_C - \phi_B) = (\phi_A - \phi_B) \qquad \ldots\ldots(11).$$

* *Annalen d. Physik*, **20**, 204 (1906).

In the discussion of the Volta effect above, each of the pieces of metal, A and B, was supposed to be electrically neutral at the beginning. Consider next what will happen when one of the pieces of metal bears an electric charge—either an excess or a deficiency of electrons, which is distributed over its surface. Before the pieces of metal are brought together there will be an electrical field between them and the line representing the initial potential energy of an electron, fig. 14, will be sloping in the gap. When A and B belong to the same element, all that happens on contact is that the charge is shared by a passage of electrons from one to the other, and the initial difference of potential

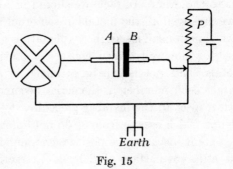

Fig. 15

between them disappears. The charge becomes distributed over their external surfaces, and there is no charge at the interface of contact. When A and B belong to different elements, the spreading of this charge over the external surfaces does not in any way affect the necessary levelling up of the electron levels, as in fig. 14c, by means of a double layer at the interface. The two effects are quite independent; that is to say, the sign and magnitude of the double layer bears no relation to the sign and magnitude of the initial potential difference that there may have been between the pieces of metal at the beginning, due to a charge possessed by either of them.

A contact potential between two metals may be demonstrated and measured by using parallel plates attached to a quadrant electrometer. Two plates, A and B, fig. 15, form a parallel-plate condenser, whose capacity can be varied by altering the distance between the plates. A is connected to one pair of quadrants of the electrometer, while B can be earthed or raised to any potential by means of the potentiometer P. We will suppose first that A and B are of the same metal. A is connected to earth and then insulated. It is found then that movement of B towards A gives a deflection of the electrometer needle, if there is any difference of potential between B and A, but has no effect while B is earthed. On the other hand, if the plates A and B are of different metals, movement of B towards A gives a deflection, even when B is earthed, showing the presence of the contact potential difference.

At the moment when A was earthed, it was put into electrical contact with B through the earthing wires. It does not matter of what metal these wires are composed, for, by the additive principle already mentioned, the contact potential between A and B is the same as if they were put into direct contact. But it will be more convenient to suppose that the connecting wires are all of the same metal as the plate A, so that there is direct contact between metal A and metal B. At the moment when this contact was made the electrons which passed across from one metal to the other set up the characteristic double layer at the metallic contact. At the same time an electrostatic field grew up in the gap between the condenser plates. The method depends upon the fact that (in the absence of any additional spurious double layer) the total drop of potential in this field is equal and opposite to that in the double layer at the metallic contact. This must clearly be so, since no difference of potential inside the conductors can exist, and the total change of potential on going round the whole circuit must be zero.

When the movement of the electrometer has been observed, a small potential of opposite sign can be applied to the plate B by means of the potentiometer, and can be increased until the electrometer ceases to register any effect when the capacity of the condenser is altered by moving one of the plates. When this condition has been reached, we know that the electrostatic field in the gap between the plates has been reduced to zero. The applied potential is equal to the characteristic contact potential difference for the pair of metals under examination.

The method described is essentially a method of detecting the presence of an electrostatic field in the gap between the metal plates *A* and *B*. An alternative way of doing this would be to place the apparatus in a high vacuum, and to detect the field by introducing into the gap some free electrons from a thermionic filament. The modern methods based on this idea have the advantage that the metal surfaces may be thoroughly cleaned by heating *in vacuo*.

One of the most important sections in any complete study of electrolytes must deal with the part played by electrolytes in generating electromotive force. Any battery or cell consists essentially of a number of metallic and electrolytic conductors connected in series. According to an elementary principle of electrostatics, when no current is flowing there can be no difference of potential anywhere in the interior of any of these conductors; if, therefore, there is a difference of potential between the terminals of the cell, this must be due to the presence of an electrical double layer at one or more of the junctions between the conductors. We have just seen how a double layer arises at the contact between any two metals, and in later chapters we shall have to consider in detail the various ways in which an electrical double layer may arise at the inter-face between a metal electrode and a conducting solution. In order to describe correctly the processes taking place in cells, it is necessary to have a clear understanding of the general properties of electrical double layers; in § 5 we shall begin by considering their electrostatic properties.

§ 5. ELECTRICAL DOUBLE LAYERS

Classical electrostatics, neglecting the atomic nature of electricity, considered each of the planes constituting a plane double layer to be continuous sheets of charge of the same density, but of opposite sign. The form of the equipotential surfaces for such a pair of planes situated in otherwise field-free space is shown in fig. 16a. It is clear that a plot of the electric potential along any line such as OP will look like curve b of fig. 16. The sharp step up in the centre of this curve shows the work required to convey unit charge from one side of the layer to the other; the work being measured by the number of equipotential lines which have been crossed once. In molecular double layers the distance between the charged surfaces is one or more molecular diameters, and we are concerned with the work required to move an electron through a distance of a few Ångstroms.

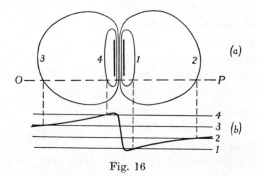

Fig. 16

The electrical double layers which occur in nature resemble these ideal types, except that each "charged plane" is, of course, not a continuous sheet but a distribution of separate charged particles. These particles may be rather sparsely distributed over the surface, forming only a fraction of a monatomic layer, and it looks at first sight as if we could convey an electron through any of the gaps between the charged particles without doing so much work as by another route. Closer examination, however, shows that this is not so. The equipotential surfaces of a single electrical doublet are illustrated in fig. 17a. In fig. 17b is shown a double layer formed from three similar doublets. In the diagram while some equipotential lines still encircle each charge, four equipotential lines of each doublet have become linked, and run up the middle between all three pairs of charges. In a double layer formed of any number of similar doublets such lines would run the whole length of the layer. Now it is clear that the difference of potential between the points O and P is the same as that between the points Q and R. On going from Q to R one cuts more equipotential lines, but the number of lines which are crossed *once* is the same, namely four, and this is all that matters. The strength of a double layer like that in fig. 17 has a value quite as definite as that of the double layer in fig. 16. The strength will, of course, depend on the distance between the dipoles. If the same three dipoles were placed somewhat nearer together, another equipotential line on each side would be linked up, giving a layer of greater strength; if they were placed somewhat farther apart, one of the linked equipotential lines would fail to join up, giving a smaller potential

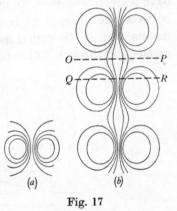

Fig. 17

difference. Equal charges spread regularly over the two surfaces give rise to a double layer, whose strength is the same as for two continuous sheets of charge possessing the same charge density. For the purpose of estimating the difference of potential across the layer, one can, therefore, forget that the charges are atomic, and consider only the density of charge per unit area. Further, we must notice that a number of charges all of one sign lying on a plane near a metal surface will induce their electrical images in the metal and give rise to a double layer. Outside the metal surface the equipotential lines will be like the right or left half of fig. 17 b.

It is important to have some idea of the number of electronic charges per unit area which are required to give a double layer possessing a potential difference of one volt. The charge per unit area is equal to the product of the potential difference and the electrostatic capacity per unit area. The latter is the same as for a parallel-plate condenser, namely $K/4\pi d$, where d is the distance between the plates. In practice the distance between the layers cannot be less than an atomic diameter. Setting d equal to 2 Ångstroms, we may estimate N the number of electronic charges per unit area required to produce a potential difference of one volt. Since 300 volts are equal to one e.s.u., we have

$$N = \frac{K}{4\pi d \cdot 300\epsilon} \qquad \dots\dots(12).$$

Putting $K = 1$, we find $N = 3 \times 10^{13}$. For many elements the number of atoms in a monatomic layer is about 10^{15}. We see then that a double layer of strength as great as one volt may be produced by quite a sparse distribution of charged particles, if these are electrons or bear the full electronic charge $\pm \epsilon$. It will be convenient to drop the study of double layers at this point, and take it up again in § 7.

§ 6. NEUTRALISATION OF IONS AT AN ELECTRODE

In later chapters we shall have to consider in detail the action of metallic electrodes dipped into solutions containing positive and negative ions. This study will be made easier if we first clear the ground by discussing the behaviour of metallic electrodes in an ionised gas. The investigation of ions in gases was begun in the last century by introducing into the ionised gas two pieces of metal, between which a difference of potential was maintained. It was found that the negative ions, after moving in the field, gave up their charges to the positive electrode, while the positive ions gave up their charges to the negative electrode; after which the neutralised molecules were presumably at liberty to behave as ordinary gas molecules. As people at that time were familiar with the transfer of electric charge from one conductor to another, the transfer of charge from an ion to an electrode was taken as a matter of course, and did not attract attention. We know now, however, that if we speak of a positive ion "giving up its charge" and moving away as a neutral atom or molecule, we mean that the ion has captured an electron from the metal. The only possible levels into which the electron can be captured are the vacant quantised levels of the ion, and we are, therefore, led to enquire how this transfer of an electron takes place. Conversely when a negative ion gives up its charge to the electrode, the electron must enter a vacant level of the metal.

In § 3 we considered a free electron near a metal surface. Suppose now that in a vacuum near a metal surface we have not a free electron, but a free negative atomic ion. Consider a line drawn perpendicular to the metal surface and passing through the centre of the ion. The potential energy of the supernumerary electron in the field of its atom is given by a curve like fig. 6 b. The required potential energy curve is to be obtained by joining together the flat portions of fig. 6b and of fig. 13a. The supernumerary electron is in a level at a depth $\mathscr{I}_-$. Suppose now that we transfer this electron to a vacant level in the metal. In removing the electron from the ion we do work $\mathscr{I}_-$; in putting it into a level near the critical level we receive energy ϕ. If then ϕ is less than $\mathscr{I}_-$, we shall have to do a net amount of work equal to $(\phi - \mathscr{I}_-)$. In

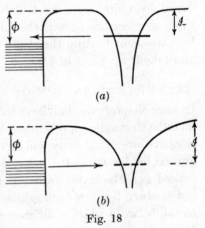

(a)

(b)

Fig. 18

fig. 18a the opposite case is illustrated, where ϕ is greater than $\mathscr{I}_-$. When we transfer the electron to the metal, a net amount of energy $(\phi - \mathscr{I}_-)$ is liberated.

It will be seen that between the ion and the metal there is a potential barrier like that which we had in fig. 14 between the two pieces of metal. According to classical mechanics the electron could not escape from the ion unless it received the necessary energy. But we saw in fig. 14 how in quantum mechanics an electron can pass through a potential barrier to a level of equal energy on the other side, provided that this level is vacant. The same thing will happen here, as soon as the ion comes near enough to the surface of the electrode.

It was mentioned in the preceding chapter that in most negative ions the supernumerary electron is very lightly bound, the value of $\mathscr{I}_-$ being less than 4 ϵ-volts. Among the metals most used for electrodes the value of ϕ lies between 4 and 6·5 ϵ-volts. The condition "ϕ greater than $\mathscr{I}_-$", represented in fig. 18a is, therefore, the normal one. The occupied level of the negative ion lies above the critical level of the metal, and consequently lies opposite to levels which are almost completely empty at room temperature. The process described is presumably the ordinary method by which gaseous negative ions are discharged at an electrode. In the converse case where ϕ happens to be less than $\mathscr{I}_-$, the occupied level of the negative ion comes below the critical level of the metal and consequently lies opposite to levels which are almost completely full at room temperature. The electron cannot escape to a level near the critical level without violating the conservation of energy. What happens in this case will be discussed in § 7.

We may study now the discharge of a singly charged positive atomic ion at an electrode. Take once more a line perpendicular to the metal surface and passing through the nucleus of this ion. The required potential energy curve is to be obtained this time by using fig. 6a in place of fig. 6b; that is, by joining together the flat portions of fig. 6a and fig. 13a. The positive ion possesses a number of vacant levels—the ground level and the excited levels. Since the excited levels do not concern us here, we shall refer to the empty ground level of the ion as *the* vacant level; it lies at a depth $\mathscr{I}$. Between the ion and the metal there is again a potential barrier through which an electron can pass, fig. 18b. The question is whether the vacant or the occupied electronic levels of the metal come opposite to the vacant level of the ion. For most elements the value of $\mathscr{I}$ is greater than 6 ϵ-volts, so that the vacant level of the ion will lie below the critical level of the metal, and the direct capture of an electron can take place.

§ 7. DOUBLE LAYER ON A METAL

For comparatively few metals has the value of the characteristic work-function been measured with high accuracy. The values obtained by the thermionic and photoelectric methods for any metal should be identical; for few metals only, however, is the agreement satisfactory. This is due to impurities present on the surface of the metal.

In § 2 it was shown how a metal consists of a lattice of positive cores situated in a cloud of free electrons. And it was explained how all the positive cores of a pure metal participate equally in the free electrons, because the cores are all identical. Suppose now that cores of some other element are present in the metal as an impurity. There is now no reason why these cores should participate in the free electrons to the same extent, even if they have the same valency. In general they do not; that is to say, round each foreign positive core the electronic density is either lower or higher than round any core of the metal itself. This fact is extremely important when some of the impurity in question is scattered over the surface of the metal. If each adsorbed core receives on the average too small or too great a share of free electrons, the resultant charges, together with their electrical images, give rise to an electrical double layer over the surface. By depositing a known number of atoms of some foreign element on to a metal surface, a double layer of any desired strength can be formed at will, and its behaviour can be investigated under controlled conditions. It is largely owing to the study of double layers of this kind that we can speak with some confidence of the structure of the double layers occurring in electrochemistry.

When each adsorbed atom receives too small a share of the free electrons and consequently bears on the average a small positive charge, these charges together with their electrical images in the metal give rise, as in fig. 17, to a double layer, of which the inner layer is negative and the outer layer positive. On the other hand, adsorbed atoms of some elements, such as oxygen, receive too large a share of the electrons; the situation is reversed, and the double layer is negative outwards. Although the charge possessed by each adsorbed atom will be only a fraction of an electronic charge, the calculation given in § 5 has shown that a large effect may be produced by a number of adsorbed atoms which form only a small fraction of a monatomic layer. When a double layer is present, the amount of work required to remove an electron from the interior of the metal will obviously be different from the value for the same surface when clean; the effective work-function of the metal is altered. To represent the condition at the surface we have only to use fig. 13a and proceed to add the ordinates of a curve, as in fig. 14.

In fig. 18 we were dealing with a clean metal surface. We may now modify this diagram to represent the approach of an ion to a metal electrode which is covered with an adsorbed film. Suppose first that the double layer is nega-tive outwards. Taking the curve of fig. 18, we must add to it the ordinates of a curve like curve a of fig. 19, giving curve b. Neglect-ing at first the presence of the ion, let us consider the metal surface. The effective work-function of the metal has been increased. If the strength of the double layer (the difference of potential across the

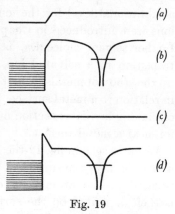

Fig. 19

layer) is V, the work required to remove an electron from the metal is now $\phi + \epsilon V$. On the other hand, if the double layer on the metal is positive outwards, we must add the ordinates of curve c, giving curve d; the effective work-function has been diminished by an amount ϵV.

Fig. 19b shows how the electronic level of the ion is raised relative to the electronic levels of the metal; in the diagram the level of the ion has been raised above the critical level of the metal. In fig. 19d the electronic level of the ion has been lowered below the critical level of the metal.

CHAPTER IV

§ 1. REMOVAL AND DEPOSITION OF METALLIC IONS

Mention has already been made in Chapter II of the stability *in vacuo* of such ions as $(Na.NH_3)^+$ and $(Ag.H_2O)^+$, formed by the union of a free metallic positive core with a neutral polar gaseous molecule. We do not know the amount of work required to remove the metallic core from the molecule, but the value is doubtless of the order of one ϵ-volt for a single charged core. This dissociation energy may be visualised as the depth of a potential valley like that of fig. 7; the polar molecule provides a vibrational level for the ion at a depth D. These polyatomic ions were introduced in Chapter II because, by the addition of further solvent molecules, as in fig. 9, we can make a gradual transition to a solvated ion. In this chapter we shall follow up the study of metals by first considering an ion like $(Ag.H_2O)^+$ in relation to a metal surface. We shall do this with the intention of making in a later section our gradual transition to a solvated ion near a metal surface.

We have seen in fig. 12 the meaning of the quantity Y. If in a vacuum near the surface of a piece of metal there is at rest an isolated positive atomic core of the same metal, and if this core is then deposited on the surface of the crystal, an amount of energy Y is liberated. Suppose now that somewhere near the surface of a piece of silver there is, not a free Ag^+ core, but a free $(Ag.H_2O)^+$ ion. And suppose that we split up this ion and transfer the Ag^+ to the surface of the silver crystal, leaving behind a free H_2O molecule. The net energy liberated in this case will be $(Y-D)$ instead of Y; for the Ag^+ was initially in a level at a depth D. If, conversely, the Ag^+ is now transferred back to the H_2O molecule to form an $(Ag.H_2O)^+$ ion, the net work done is $(Y-D)$.

This process may be visualised by combining fig. 7 with fig. 12. Let us fix attention on one of the positive cores which form the surface of a metallic crystal; and suppose that we remove the core from the crystal along a line drawn perpendicular to the surface at this point. The potential energy of the core along this line is represented by a curve which rapidly becomes horizontal, fig. 12. But suppose that somewhere on this line, at a point P, fig. 20, there happens to be a polar molecule. The potential energy curve will no longer remain flat. For if this polar molecule has its negative side directed towards the metal, or if the molecule is free to rotate, we know that the positive ion will be attracted when it comes near

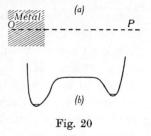

Fig. 20

to the molecule, while at still closer distances there will be a violent repulsion. In the neighbourhood of the molecule, whose position we are supposing fixed at P, the curve will, in fact, be of the usual molecular form, i.e. like fig. 7, only reversed from left to right, because in this case the moving ion is on the left of the stationary molecule. The potential energy along the whole line OP must be obtained by joining together the flat portions of fig. 12 and of fig. 7 reversed. The complete curve thus has a minimum at each end, with a horizontal portion between them, fig. 20b.

Before discussing the properties of this curve, let us carry through an alternative argument which will throw light on the result. Let us start with an $(Ag.H_2O)^+$ ion in $vacuo$. We have already considered the process of dissociating such an ion into Ag^+ and H_2O. As we remove the silver ion from the water molecule, the attraction between them falls off, and the potential energy curve rapidly becomes horizontal. But suppose next that our polyatomic ion was initially in the neighbourhood of a piece of metallic silver at a certain point P, and was so orientated that when we remove the Ag^+ from the H_2O along the line PO, this line PO passes through a lattice point of the silver crystal, where there is a vacancy for a silver positive core. Then the potential energy will no longer remain horizontal, but will have a second minimum near the surface of the metal due to the attraction of the metal surface on the Ag$^+$ ion; the depth of this second minimum will be Y. In fact, the potential energy curve at which we arrive by this argument is identical with fig. 20b. In both arguments we are concerned with a polar molecule, a metal surface and a metallic positive core between them. And it does not matter whether this positive core is supposed initially to belong to the polar molecule, or to the surface layer of the crystal lattice. If it belongs to the polar molecule, it will be initially in the potential valley on the right; and if we move it over into the potential valley on the left, we are depositing the metallic ion at a vacant lattice point on the metal surface. We may reverse the process by moving the metallic ion back to the potential valley on the right; in this case we are detaching the positive core from the surface and combining it with the polar molecule to form a polyatomic ion. The potential energy curve is thus ambivalent, whether we are depositing a positive core at a vacant lattice point or removing a positive core from an occupied lattice point. Fig. 20 shows clearly that in one case $(Y - D)$ is the net energy liberated, and in the other case the net work done.

In fig. 20 the curve was obtained by joining together the flat portions of figs. 12 and 7. If the polar molecule is nearer to the metal surface, so that the curves intersect, as do the dotted curves of fig. 21a, we must obtain the resultant potential energy by adding the ordinates of the two curves; in this way we obtain the full curve of fig. 21a with a smaller potential hill in the middle. The nearer the polar molecule is to the metal surface, the smaller will be the potential hill. It becomes clear then how we can picture the impact of a polar molecule or of an ion such as $(Ag.H_2O)^+$ on to a metal surface. At the

(a)

(b)

Fig. 21

moment of impact the potential hill may completely vanish, reappearing immediately as the molecule rebounds. In this case the Ag^+ ion may pass spontaneously from one potential valley to a level of equal energy in the other potential valley, if a level of equal energy exists. And we see now the important point, that when, as in fig. 21 a, the two potential valleys are not of the same depth, transitions in one direction are more restricted than transitions in the opposite direction. At room temperature the ions will be nearly all in their lowest vibration levels. Consider an ion initially in the lowest vibration level of the potential valley on the right of fig. 21 a. If at the moment of impact the intervening potential hill disappears, the particle will be able to move across into a level of approximately equal energy in the potential valley on the left, from which it can fall to a lower level there. If, on the other hand, we consider an ion which is in the lowest level of the deep potential valley on the left at the moment of impact, this ion must obviously remain there. For an ion to move across from left to right, it must be in a rather high vibration level at the moment of impact; for only then will it find a level of equal energy in the shallower potential valley on the right. In fact, it must possess a vibration energy at least as great as $(Y - D)$, since this is the amount which will bring it up to a level opposite to the lowest level on the right.

§ 2. SOLUTION OF METALLIC ION

We have so far been discussing the presence near the point P of a single polar molecule, to which a positive atomic ion may be attached. We may clearly go on to consider now the presence near P of two or more similar molecules, to which the metallic core may be attached to form an ion like $(Ag \cdot nH_2O)^+$. As explained in discussing fig. 9, the work D required to detach the positive core from these molecules will be greater than from a single molecule, i.e. they will provide a deeper potential valley than will a single molecule. The potential energy curve along the line OP will resemble figs. 20 and 21 a, except that the potential valley on the right may now be as deep as that on the left, or it may be still deeper, fig. 21 b.

If our polar molecules are solvent molecules, the potential valley on the right will finally become that of a solvated ion. As in fig. 10, the dissociation potential D becomes replaced by the solvation energy W; and the quantity $(Y-D)$ is replaced by $(Y-W)$. In this way, with a little adaptation, we obtain a useful picture of the deposition of a metallic ion from solution, or the converse passage of a metallic ion into solution. In figs. 20 and 21a we studied processes involving a single polar molecule, solely because they may be considered the prototypes of processes involving solvent molecules and solvated ions. When a piece of metal is dipped into a solution containing its own ions, these solvated ions will be continually moving towards and away from the surface. At any time it may happen that when a solvated ion approaches the surface, the metallic core, becoming detached from the solvent molecules, adheres to the crystal at a vacant lattice point. Conversely, at any time, one of the positive cores forming the surface of the crystal may move away into the solvent, becoming solvated as it does so. When a piece of metal at room temperature is in air or in a vacuum, a positive core does not escape from the surface, because the amount of energy Y is prohibitively large. But when the metal is in contact with a solvent, if the value of W in this solvent is as large or nearly as large as Y, the ion may pass into solution even at room temperature. With regard to the small potential hill in the middle of the curves of fig. 21, our knowledge of solvent molecules and metal surfaces is not yet sufficient to say whether, from time to time, this potential hill completely disappears. But this does not matter, since for many soluble metals we know from observation how easily ions go into solution and are deposited. We shall study these processes further in Chapter VII.

§ 3. METAL IN IONIC SOLUTION

When we dip a metal electrode into a solution, we are putting two conductors into contact. The same is true if we dip a metal into pure solvent, for no solvent is a good insulator. When no current is flowing, there can be no drop of potential inside either of these conductors, but there may be an electrical double layer over the surface of contact between them. The case of two metals in contact with one another was discussed in Chapter III, where it was shown that the sign and magnitude of the electrical double layer, which arises at the surface of contact, bear no relation to the sign and magnitude of any initial potential difference due to a charge on the surface of one of the metals. The same will be true at the interface of a metal dipping into a solution.

The process which determines the value of the double layer may be one of several different types, according to the nature of the metal and the species of ion present. Among the most important types is the case of a soluble metal dipping into a solution containing its own ions, as one has, for example, in each half of a Daniell cell. Here the approach to equilibrium will be similar to that between any liquid and its vapour, except that the particles bear electrical charges. Consider unit area of the interface between the metal and the solution. In every second a certain number of metallic ions become detached from the surface of the lattice and pass into solution; and in every second a certain number of metallic ions in solution, which happen to approach the surface of the metal, adhere to it. At the moment when the piece of metal is first dipped into the solution, there is no reason why these numbers should be the same; but when equilibrium is reached, they must be equal to one another. If the number of positive ions leaving the metal is initially greater than the number being deposited, the metal will rapidly acquire a negative charge due to the electrons left behind in it. This negative charge hinders the further removal of positive ions, until the rate of escape from the surface is equal to the rate of deposition. On the other hand, if the number of metallic ions being deposited is initially greater than the number leaving the surface, the metal will rapidly acquire a positive charge, which will hinder the further deposition of positive ions on its surface, until equilibrium is reached. This is the explanation given long ago by Nernst. Unfortunately erroneous ideas as to the "electrode potentials" of the metals have been founded on this conception, which in itself gives a true picture of the equilibrium.

The effect of depositing positive cores upon one surface of a piece of metal in a vacuum was mentioned in Chapter III. It was pointed out that when the cores belong to the same element as the metal and are not too numerous, they will participate fully in the free electrons, and the positive charge which the metal has acquired will not be localised on the particular surface on which the cores have been deposited, but will be spread over the surfaces of the conductor according to the laws of electrostatics. On the other hand, the idea mentioned in the preceding paragraph, of ions deposited from solution on to an electrode, presupposes that an electrical double layer will be formed at the interface where the metal is in contact with the solution.

To examine this question let us suppose that our solution was at first electrically neutral—the positive ions in it being exactly neutralised by the negative ions. If on inserting the electrode positive ions are deposited, an equal negative charge is left behind in the solution and it is this negative charge which prevents the positive charge from spreading over all surfaces of the metal; the positive charge is bound to the interface. Each negative ion in solution near the surface of the electrode has its electrical image in the metal. It is best to think of the double layer as arising in this way; the positive charge on the metal is not associated with the particular cores which have been deposited.

CHAPTER V

§ 1. ASSEMBLIES OF IONS

A study of electrolytic ions, like that attempted in this book, falls into two parts. In the first place we want to know the structure and properties of a single ion immersed in a solvent— we want to know these for each species of ion in each solvent. And secondly, since in practice we deal only with assemblies of positive and negative ions, we want to know the behaviour of these assemblies. In the last paragraph of the preceding chapter we came for the first time to a problem of this second class, in which we had to deal with the behaviour of a large number of ions. The earlier part of the book had been concerned with the nature of individual solvated ions, and in later chapters much more will have to be added about their solvation. At this point, however, it will be convenient to pass on to subjects under the second heading, and to approach the fundamental problem as to why electrolytic solutions exist at all.

In a gas or vapour we can, by electron impact and other means, produce large quantities of free ions. But these positive and negative particles very quickly recombine with each other, or else are deposited on the walls of the vessel. At room temperature the gas or vapour soon loses its conductivity, and nothing that we can do, short of supplying fresh ions, will maintain it. In a solution, on the other hand, the ions continually collide with each other, but the electrons are not transferred from the negative ions to the positive; nor do the ions disappear by recombination or by deposition on the walls of the vessel. In comparison with the ionised gas the situation is reversed, but is equally out of our control. We shall attack this problem most easily by asking first what is known about collisions which ions make *in vacuo*.

§ 2. COLLISIONS IN WHICH ELECTRONS
ARE TRANSFERRED

It is found that when neon positive ions, Ne^+, are introduced
with low velocity into a vessel containing argon gas, argon
positive ions are produced.* When an argon atom makes an
ordinary gas-kinetic collision with a neon ion, an electron may
evidently be transferred from one to the other, neutralising the
neon ion

$$Ne^+ + Ar \rightarrow Ne + Ar^+ \qquad \ldots\ldots(13).$$

From Table XI, page 201, we see that the first ionisation poten-
tial of argon is 15·7 ϵ-volts, while that of neon is 21·5 ϵ-volts.
The energy liberated when an electron is introduced into Ne^+ is
5·8 ϵ-volts greater than the amount of work that would have to
be done in obtaining a *free* electron from the valence level of an
argon atom *in vacuo*. But in the collision the electron does not

actually become free in passing
from one atomic core to the
other. The situation is illustrated
in fig. 22, which represents the
potential energy of an electron
along the line passing through

Fig. 22

the cores of the two atoms at the moment of impact. The core
of each atom contributes a curve like fig. 6 a. The horizontal line
on the left represents the occupied level of the argon atom, while
the lower horizontal broken line on the right represents the
normal vacant level of Ne^+. As in the process of fig. 14, quantum
mechanics allows the electron to slip through the intervening
potential barrier, and to fall into the unoccupied level of Ne^+.
The excess energy, 5·8 ϵ-volts, is turned into kinetic energy of
translation, the colliding particles flying apart with high velocity
after collision. This type of impact is known as a collision "of
the second kind", in contrast to the more familiar collisions of
the first kind, in which kinetic energy is turned into internal
energy (excitation by impact).

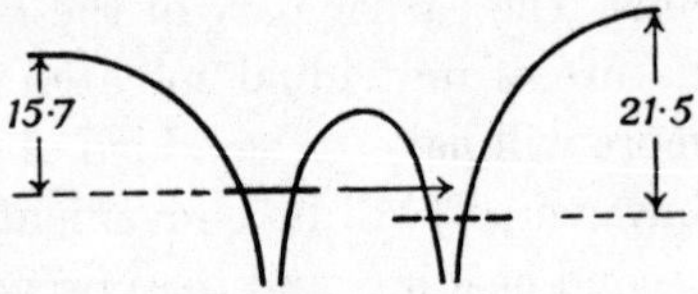

* Smyth, *Rev. Modern Physics*, **3**, 359 (1931).

We may notice, in passing, that in a similar way an electron may be transferred from a negative ion to a neutral atom. If, for example, a bromine negative ion Br^- in a vacuum were to collide with a free chlorine atom, an electron could be transferred:

$$Br^- + Cl \rightarrow Br + Cl^- \qquad \text{......(14)},$$

since, as we see from Table XI, the energy of attachment of an electron to Cl is greater than to Br. The energy liberated would be taken up as kinetic energy of the colliding particles. In the examples mentioned an electron was transferred from one atomic particle to another. But the processes occur, not only in atomic, but also in molecular impacts. For example, in argon gas containing water vapour the transfer

$$A^+ + H_2O \rightarrow A + (H_2O)^+ \qquad \text{......(15)}$$

is found to occur, the occupied electronic level in the water molecule being higher than the vacant level in A^+. When we say that the occupied level in one species of particle is "higher" than the vacant level in another species of particle, we mean that the work required to remove an electron from the former is less than the energy which would be liberated when a free electron is introduced into the latter. We visualise the relative height of the levels as in fig. 22. If we say of two molecular positive ions that the first possesses a lower vacant level than the latter, we mean that a greater amount of energy would be liberated by introducing a free electron into the former than into the latter. The energy of an electron at rest *in vacuo* is always taken as the zero from which levels are measured. Thus the argon singly charged ion, Ar^+, possesses a vacant level at $-15 \cdot 7$ ϵ-volts. And, of course, the neutral argon possesses an occupied level at $-15 \cdot 7$ ϵ-volts.

Since the total energy of the two particles after impact cannot be greater than before impact, and since the kinetic energies at room temperature are so small, we can say at once that at room temperature such electron transitions will be found only when the ion possesses a vacant level of equal or of lower energy than the initial occupied level. From Table XI one can see at once which positive ions can be neutralised in this way by collision with which atoms (or negative ions). One has only to compare the ionisation potential of the two species. For molecules and molecular ions we can make similar predictions as soon as their ionisation potentials are known.

§ 3. ELECTRONIC LEVELS OF IONS IN SOLUTION

Of the large number of positive ions of Table XI which have been studied *in vacuo* in various stages of ionisation, comparatively few are known either in solution or in crystalline salts. We see a possible limitation on species of positive ions in any solvent, if we consider the valence electrons of the solvent molecules in relation to the vacant electronic level of each solvated ion. For if into any solvent we were to introduce a positive ion whose vacant level lies lower than these occupied levels of the solvent, a valence electron from an adjacent solvent molecule would immediately fall into the vacant level of the ion, neutralising it. This species of ion will be unknown in that solvent; it will not be found because it cannot exist for any measurable length of time.

Since in solution positive ions are always accompanied by negatives, we can go on at once to say that, for any pair of ionic species in solution, the occupied level of the negative ion in that solvent must be *lower* than the vacant level of the positive ion in that solvent. For any species of which this is not true, the ions cannot co-exist, and solutions containing the pair will be unknown. This shows how radically the relative positions of the levels of positive and negative ions in solution must differ from their positions *in vacuo*. It was emphasised in Chapter II that the supernumerary electron in any negative ion is lightly bound in a high level, while a glance at Table XI shows that in all doubly charged ions the vacant level lies at a depth greater than 9 ϵ-volts, and in most singly charged ions at a depth greater than 5 ϵ-volts. Whether the ions are in gas, vapour or solution, it is clear that no assembly of positive ions A^+ and negative ions B^- can be stable unless the occupied levels of B^- are lower than the vacant levels of A^+. In ionic solutions then the levels must have become reversed, so that the electrons in all negative ions, without exception, are unable to escape to vacant levels in the positives, even when these are doubly or trebly charged. It is the purpose of this chapter to consider how this comes about.

Since, according to classical electrostatics, in a medium of dielectric constant K all electrostatic forces are reduced, we might have expected that in a solvent all binding forces would be reduced, leading to smaller ionisation potentials all round. This is not what is required nor is it what is found; for we shall show below that the binding energy of the supernumerary electron in any negative ion is actually greater in solution than *in vacuo*, thus leading to the stability of assemblies of positive and negative ions.

Instead of attempting to make at once a direct estimate of the relative positions of the levels in a positive and a negative ion, the subject may be approached most simply by first comparing the electron level of each with the electron levels of a metal. For, as shown in fig. 18, the critical level of a clean metal provides a kind of standard reference level, to which the occupied or vacant electron level of any atom, ion, or molecule may conveniently be referred. We shall retain the symbol $\mathscr{J}$ for expressing the depth of the electronic level of the ion *in vacuo*, and shall use J to denote the corresponding quantity in solution. If J is found to be greater than the work function ϕ, then the electronic level of the solvated ion is lower than the critical level of the metal by an amount $(J - \phi)$ and so on.

Let us consider the neutralisation of a singly charged ion when situated in a certain solvent; we shall first consider the process carried out indirectly by means of a cycle—that is, instead of neutralising the ion within the solvent, we shall remove it to a vacuum, neutralising it there with an electron taken from the metal, and replace the neutral atom in the solvent. The final result will be the same as if the electron had passed straight from the electrode to the ion in solution; a process which we can conveniently represent by a horizontal arrow like that of fig. 18b.

We wish to know whether the energy received in the cycle is greater or less than for an ion *in vacuo*. The work done in removing an electron from the metal into the vacuum will be the same in both cases; but consider the other steps in the cycle; in removing the ion from the solvent we do work equal to the solvation energy W; in neutralising it *in vacuo* we receive energy $\mathscr{I}$; in replacing the neutral atom in the solvent we receive energy equal to the heat of solution of the neutral atom, but this is a quantity small compared with $\mathscr{I}$ and W, and may be neglected for the present. The energy received is thus $(\mathscr{I} - W)$, instead of $\mathscr{I}$. The vacant level of the positive ion is thus *higher* than the level *in vacuo* by an amount W.

For a singly charged positive ion

$$J = \mathscr{I} - W \qquad \qquad \ldots\ldots(16).$$

If we use a diagram, the escape of an electron from an electrode to a positive ion in solution may be represented by a horizontal arrow like that of fig. 18*b*, provided that the vacant level of the solvated ion is inserted at a depth J given by (16). The analogous relation for multiply charged ions will be given in Chapter IX.

We shall now find that for every negative ion the position is reversed; their occupied levels are all lowered in solution. To show this we shall convey an electron from a singly charged ion to a metal by means of a cycle similar to the last. We remove the negative ion from the solvent to a vacuum, doing work W_-; we take the supernumerary electron from the ion, doing work equal to the ionisation potential (electron-affinity) $\mathscr{I}_-$; and we replace the neutral atom in the solvent, again receiving a small amount of energy which we shall neglect for the present. On putting the free electron from the vacuum into the metal we receive an amount of energy which is, of course, the same, whether the ion has been removed from a solvent or not. But the work done in the previous steps was $(\mathscr{I}_- + W_-)$ instead of only $\mathscr{I}_-$. The final result is the same as if the electron had escaped from the solvated ion direct to the metal. It is clear that the occupied level of the ion in solution is *lower* than *in vacuo* by an amount W_-. For a singly charged negative ion

$$J_- = \mathscr{I}_- + W_- \qquad \qquad \ldots\ldots(17).$$

The occupied level of every negative ion is thus shifted in the opposite direction to the vacant level of every positive ion. If we use a diagram, the escape of an electron from a solvated ion to an electrode may be represented by a horizontal arrow, like that in fig. 18a, provided that the occupied electronic level of the ion is inserted at a depth J_- given by (17).

By using the critical level of a metal as a standard reference level, we have been able to study the electron levels of positive and negative ions separately. It is now a simple matter to compare the occupied level of a negative ion directly with the vacant level of any singly charged positive ion in the same solvent. The former will be higher than the latter if $(\mathscr{I}_- + W_-)$ is less than $(\mathscr{I} - W)$; in this case the ions cannot co-exist in solution. But if J_- is greater than J the vacant level of the positive ion is higher than the occupied level of the negative, and is immune from invasion. The required condition is that $(\mathscr{I}_- + W_-)$ be greater than $(\mathscr{I} - W)$. Since W and W_- are each several ϵ-volts, this condition may easily be satisfied, although $\mathscr{I}_-$ is less than $\mathscr{I}$. In this chapter we shall not study the numerical values, but these will be given in Chapter XIV.

This shift of the electron levels of atoms and ions in solution is due entirely to the necessity of conserving energy. If, starting with a pure solvent, we introduce an ion into it, a large amount of energy is dissipated as heat, as described in Chapter I. If at any subsequent time the charge in solution is neutralised, an equal amount of work must be done, in order to conserve energy. The difference in sign between the upward shift of positive-ion levels and the downward shift of negative-ion levels arises from the fact that when the ion is neutralised in one case an electron is added to the particle and in the other it is taken away, and is quite independent of any particular mechanism. Even a continuous structureless dielectric medium would give rise to an energy of solvation, as shown in Chapter I, and consequently to a shift of the electronic levels of the solvated ions—downwards for negative and upwards for positive ions. On the other hand, we shall show qualitatively how the shift of the level arises in terms of solvent molecules. Figs. 16 and 17 represented a double layer of the type where the opposite charges are distributed over parallel planes. In the same way we can imagine a type where the opposite charges are distributed over concentric spheres. To convey a charge to the inside, or from the inside of such a spherical double layer, will require a certain amount of work. Now the polarised solvent molecules surrounding any ion may be regarded as roughly equivalent to a little spherical double layer with the ion in the middle.

Round a positive ion the spherical double layer is positive outwards, as in fig. 23. If we wish to convey an electron to this ion to neutralise it, we have to do work in going through the double layer. Consequently, instead of receiving the energy $\mathscr{I}$ which we should receive in a vacuum, we receive a less amount; this means that the vacant level of the ion has been raised. Round a negative ion in solution the sign of the double layer is reversed. The layer is negative outwards and additional work

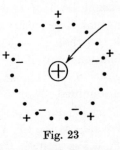

Fig. 23

is required to remove an electron from inside; in this way the ionisation potential is increased, and the occupied level is deeper than in a vacuum.

§ 4. THERMAL ENERGY AND EQUILIBRIUM

As soon as we know the values of W and W_-, we can draw up a list of values of J and J_- for ions in solution, similar to that for ions in a vacuum; this will tell us the positions of the occupied and vacant electronic levels. A species of negative ion, having a very low occupied level, will be able to exist in the presence of many species of positive ions; whereas the negative ion which has its electron in a rather high level will only be able to exist in the presence of those particular species of positive ions whose vacant electronic levels are higher. Again, a species of positive ion with a very high vacant level will be able to co-exist with many species of negative ions; whereas those ions, which have rather low vacant levels, will only exist in solution in company with those species of negative ions whose occupied electronic levels are still lower.

When in this way we speak of one species of ion being incompatible with another, we must notice what happens when the ionisation potentials of the two particles have nearly the same value. The transference of the electrons depends upon their familiar tendency to fall into the lowest level available. When, however, there is available a pair of levels of nearly the same energy, the electrons will distribute themselves among the two levels, according to the Boltzmann law. Such a situation may arise in a transference of electrons, such as we have considered:

$$A^+ + B \rightarrow A + B^+ \qquad \ldots\ldots(18).$$

For most pairs of particles the electronic levels of the two species will differ by one ϵ-volt or more. It may happen, on the other hand, that the vacant level of A^+ lies only a little below the occupied level of B. In this case, if we mix equal numbers of the particles A^+ and B, and examine the assembly afterwards, we shall find that the electrons have distributed themselves among the two available levels—that is to say, among the two species of particles—according to the Boltzmann law. In other words the reaction (18) has not gone to completion.

Although there may exist borderline cases, we see that such reactions may be divided roughly into two classes—those where the two electronic levels differ by a large amount and the reaction goes to completion under all experimental conditions, and those where the levels have nearly the same energy and the reaction goes to a recognisable equilibrium. In the former the result is not dependent to any observable degree upon the concentrations of the substances, while in the latter class the equilibrium depends upon their relative concentrations.

It is worth while looking briefly at the ionic mechanism which maintains this equilibrium. In the B^+ ion which has been formed by (18) the vacant level is higher than the occupied level in the A atom. But in a gas at room temperature it is not true to say that on collision the electron cannot be transferred back

again from A to B⁺. Energy must, of course, be conserved.
But at room temperature the particles possess a certain amount
of kinetic energy, and a few particles possess a large amount. If
at an encounter between B⁺ and A the two particles possess
between them a sufficient amount of kinetic energy, it may
happen that some of this energy is used to transfer an electron
from A to the higher level in B⁺, the particles moving apart
after collision with much smaller velocities than before. Comparatively few particles will have sufficient kinetic energy; the
reaction (18), therefore, goes from left to right, until the number
of A and B⁺ particles is much greater than the number of A⁺ and
B. If the difference in energy between the two electronic levels
is anything approaching 0.5 ϵ-volt, the reaction goes to completion. For the value of kT at room temperature is about
$1/40$ ϵ-volt, or 600 calories per mol; and if we insert the energy
$E = 0.5$ into the Boltzmann factor $e^{-E/kT}$, we obtain the small
value e^{-20}, or about 10^{-9}. It is only when the initial and final
energy levels are close together that we find an appreciable
amount remaining in the upper level at room temperature.

In solution the thermal energy of the ions leads to the same
result, although the mechanism is not quite the same. It is now
recognised that in any liquid the thermal energy is mainly of a
vibrational character like that of a solid, rather than trans-
lational like that of a gas; the molecules of a liquid possess a
large amount of potential energy like the vibrating atoms of a
solid. In an ionic solution some ions will be in the higher vibrational levels of fig. 10. At an encounter between two ions this
excess energy may be used to transfer an electron from one to a
higher level in the other, exactly as in a gas. The relative number
of such reverse transfers taking place depends upon the concentrations of the various species at the moment, and upon the
mean thermal energy of the particles. It is important to realise
that the necessity of paying attention to the various concentrations is closely bound up with the thermal energy of the particles. As we shall see later, it is just this connection between the
concentration c and the thermal energy RT which gives rise to

the familiar terms of the form $RT \log c$, which occur in expressions for the e.m.f. of cells. At the absolute zero of temperature the final result of any reaction would be completely independent of the concentrations of the various species.

§ 5. ABSORPTION SPECTRA OF SOLVATED IONS

In § 2 we found that in solution the positions of the electronic levels of ions are quite different from *in vacuo*. We may now enquire whether any of the familiar properties of solutions are a result of this shift of levels. In the first place there is the fact that so many solutions of electrolytes are transparent and uncoloured. It was pointed out in Chapter II that in many negative ions *in vacuo* the supernumerary electron is so loosely bound that the work to remove it is only two or three ϵ-volts, and that consequently the continuous absorption spectrum for ejection of the electron from the ion lies partly in the visible region of the spectrum. If this were true also of ions in solution, most ionic solutions would show the characteristic absorption of the negative ions present in the visible or the near ultra-violet. This, we know, is not so; for example, solutions of iodides do not show any absorption here due to the iodine negative ions.

But the fact is easily explained if we recognise that owing to the increase from $\mathscr{I}_-$ to $\mathscr{I}_- + W_-$ a quantum of energy $h\nu = \mathscr{I}_-$ is insufficient to eject an electron, and therefore no absorption in this region occurs.

For some solvated negative ions, such as those of iodine and bromine, a characteristic absorption band lying farther in the ultra-violet is easily located. Unfortunately water and other suitable solvents are opaque to

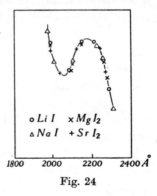

Fig. 24

wave-lengths beyond about 1750 Å., and any characteristic bands lying farther in the ultra-violet than this cannot be located. As an example of the absorption spectra of negative ions, fig. 24

gives the curve for four iodides, LiI, NaI, MgI$_2$ and SrI$_2$, dissolved in ethyl alcohol, values of the absorption coefficient being plotted against the wave-lengths between 2400 Å. and 1900 Å.* For all four solutions the points lie on a smooth curve, which must be the characteristic spectrum of the solvated iodine negative ion I$^-$; in aqueous solution the results are very similar. The interpretation of such spectra will be considered in detail in Volume II.

§ 6. EQUILIBRIUM BETWEEN IONS AND AN ELECTRODE

We may conclude this chapter by considering the electronic levels of ions in relation to those of a metal. What happens when an insulated metal electrode is introduced into a stream of positive ions in a vacuum is well known. Of the first ions which strike the surface some give up their charge to the metal. The field due to this charge exerts a repulsion on the next incident ions. But the process continues, some ions giving up their charge to the metal, until the repulsion becomes sufficiently strong to prevent the ions from reaching the surface. The electrode is then in equilibrium with the stream of ions. Similarly, if an electrode is exposed to an assembly of negative ions, it will go on acquiring a negative charge from them, until the potential of the electrode becomes sufficient to keep the incident negative ions at bay. The ions no longer discharge themselves against the metal. Consider now an insulated electrode exposed to an assembly containing both positive and negative ions. It obviously cannot charge itself up both positively and negatively; any charge which it happens to acquire will be immediately neutralised by the ions of opposite sign, which will be attracted and discharged at its surface. There is no possibility of an assembly of positive and negative gaseous ions existing permanently in the presence of an insulated metal electrode at room temperature.

We must explain the observed fact that every solution containing positive and negative ions can exist in contact with an

* Lederle, *Zeit. f. Phys. Chem.* B, **10**, 129 (1930).

insulated electrode indefinitely. Suppose that we have an ionic solution which is electrically neutral, and suppose we take a piece of metal which is electrically neutral, and dip it into the solution. If the work-function ϕ for the metal is larger than J_- for the negative ions present in the solution (fig. 25a), a few electrons will escape to the metal, charging it negatively. This negative charge on the metal, in conjunction with the equal positive charge which has been left behind in the solution (the charges of the few positive ions now without negative partners), immediately gives rise to a double layer, negative inwards, which lowers the electronic levels of the ions relative to the electronic levels of the metal, as in fig. 19d. Conversely, if ϕ for the metal is less than J for the positive ions present in the solution (fig. 25b), electrons will escape from the metal to the

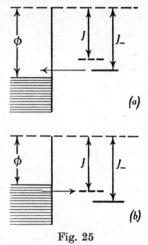

Fig. 25

vacant level of a few of the positive ions. An electrical double layer grows up on the metal, negative outwards, which raises the electronic levels of the ions relative to those of the metal. In either case a stable situation will be reached, when the critical level of the metal has been brought half-way between the electronic levels of the two ions, so that it lies above the occupied level of the negative ion and below the vacant level of the positive ion. As we have pointed out in this chapter, the electronic levels of solvated ions are always such that this condition can be satisfied, although in a vacuum for nearly all species of ions it cannot be satisfied.

CHAPTER VI

§ 1. EXPERIMENTAL METHODS AVAILABLE

We can hardly compare the behaviour of ions in solution with their behaviour in gases without, sooner or later, examining the experimental methods by which this behaviour has been studied in each case; and this seems the most convenient place to make an enquiry of this kind. Among other things we may ask what measure of justification there is for the present position, where the study of ions in gases is regarded as physics, and the study of ions in solution as a branch of chemistry.

As a first example, we shall consider the method by which an ionic process like that of (13) is studied in a gas or vapour. In the wall of the vessel a slit is provided, through which the ions escape into a vacuum, which is maintained by means of differential pumping. The ions escaping are passed through the electric and magnetic fields of a mass spectrograph, and in less than a millionth of a second each species has recorded its presence. No similar method has yet been devised for rapidly extracting specimen ions from a solution during an ionic reaction. As a result, research on ions in solution has followed a profoundly different course from that on ions in gases. Attention has been directed not upon the properties of individual ions, but upon the properties of assemblies of ions, and not upon the behaviour of assemblies during reaction, but mainly upon the equilibrium which is finally reached.

Although there is no method corresponding to the mass spectrograph, we have for ions in solution a method of identifying them without removing them from the solution—namely, by the characteristic absorption spectrum. This method is not available for ions in gases, because in a vapour or gas in the laboratory we never obtain a sufficient number of ions per unit volume. The number of molecules in a gas at N.T.P. is $2 \cdot 7 \times 10^{19}$, and in an experiment at room temperature we obtain only an exceedingly small fraction of them in an ionised state; under the most favourable conditions we can obtain about 10^{12} ions per cm.^{3}. It is only in a solar or stellar atmosphere, where we have a column of vapour many miles in length, that we observe absorption lines of ions. On the other hand, one must become familiar with the fact that, in a molar solution dissociated into ion pairs, the number of ions of each kind in one cm.^{3} is more than 22 times the total number of molecules in a gas at atmospheric pressure. For a molar solution of any neutral substance contains 6×10^{20} molecules per cm.^{3}, or the equivalent of a gas at a pressure of about 22 atmospheres. As a result, absorption spectra of ions may be identified in very dilute solutions; and an observation of the absorption spectrum of any solution may, therefore, be a delicate test for the presence of certain species of ions. It may be mentioned, for example, that a convenient concentration for photographing the spectrum of fig. 24 is 1/40,000 molar solution.

When an electronic transfer, analogous to (13), takes place between ions in solution, it will of course be accompanied by a complete change in the absorption spectrum. How far the method of identification by absorption spectra can be carried we do not yet know, because the method has not been exploited. Chemical analysis has had as its main object the removal of each substance from solution in electrically neutral form, i.e. in the form of a solid precipitate of a less soluble compound. With this end in view strong solutions are used, in order that the saturation point of the said substance may be reached and passed. Very little attention has been paid to those reactions in solution which yield neither a precipitate nor an evolution of gas. In fact, the existence of such reactions tends to be forgotten. Yet, when we set out to study the properties of ions in solution, we ought surely to begin with those reactions where all the substances remain at the end as positive and negative ions in solution. The formation of a precipitate is merely an irrelevant process to be avoided. From this point of view we ought, therefore, to pay attention primarily to just those reactions which are least studied in chemical analysis, namely those which do not give rise to any sparingly soluble product. Secondly, when a sparingly soluble substance is to be formed, we ought, whenever possible, to start with such dilute solutions that the saturation point will not be reached. The formation of a precipitate from a super-saturated solution is a separate problem which may be studied by itself.

§ 2. DIRECT AND INDIRECT METHODS

The next point can be most easily made clear by carrying out an imaginary experiment with gaseous ions. Suppose that we have a vessel through the wall of which projects an insulated electrode. We have already mentioned, in § 6 of Chapter v, how this electrode will come to equilibrium with any positive gaseous ions which we introduce into the vessel; the insulated electrode acquires a positive charge from the ions, until it is sufficient to prevent the further neutralisation of positive ions. Suppose now that we have a separate vessel through the wall of which projects another insulated electrode. If we introduce a certain species of negative gaseous ions into this vessel, the insulated electrode will likewise come to equilibrium with them. In this vessel neutralisation of ions at the electrode has come to a standstill because the electrode bears too large a negative charge, while in the other vessel it is because the electrode bears too large a positive charge.

Our aim in imagining this experiment is to ask what will happen if we now stretch a wire between the terminals of the two electrodes. As soon as contact is made the charge on one electrode can neutralise the opposite charge on the other, with the result that the discharge of ions in each vessel can begin again. The electrons received by one electrode from the negative ions can flow along the wire to the other electrode, where they can be given up to the positive ions there. In fact, a continuous electric current will flow in the wire, until the supply of ions is exhausted.

This type of experiment is not one that is ever performed. We saw in Chapter v that in the electron transfer

$$Ne^+ + Ar \rightarrow Ar^+ + Ne$$

a large amount of energy is released. But no one would think of putting the argon gas into one vessel, the Ne^+ ions into another, joining the two by means of a wire, and expecting the electrons from the argon atoms to flow along the wire to the neon ions, although, if the experiment were practicable, the 5·8 ϵ-volts of energy per ion would be liberated as usual. But, we may almost say, this apparently round about way of procedure is utilised in a type of experiment which is commonly carried out with positive and negative ions in solution. Suppose that we are studying two species of ions in solution—let us call them A^{++} and X^-—and we wish to know whether the electron levels are such that the electron transfer

$$A^{++} + X^- \rightarrow A^+ + X \qquad \ldots\ldots(19)$$

can take place. There are two methods at our disposal. In either case we start with two solutions of roughly the same concentration; we take one vessel containing the ion A^{++} in solution with an equivalent amount of some species of negative ion, and another vessel containing the ion X^- in solution with some species of positive ion, in which we are not interested at the moment. Taking these two solutions, we can simply mix them, and see if anything happens to the ions A^{++} and X^-. Alternatively, we can introduce a platinum electrode into the solution containing A^{++}, and another platinum electrode into the solution which contains the ions X^- at the same concentration; and, having put the two solutions into connection (through a third conducting solution which reacts with neither), we can stretch a wire from the first piece of platinum to the second, and see whether there is a flow of electrons from the latter to the former. We may find that in one vessel the X^- ions are steadily giving up their electrons to the electrode*, and that in the other vessel the A^{++} ions are steadily being converted to A^+ by capture of electrons. This steady flow of electrons will not take place

* See p. 96.

unless the relative positions of the occupied and vacant electronic levels of the ions are such that the transference of electrons would take place on mixing the two solutions.

To this extent the indirect method, using equivalent concentrations in two coupled vessels, is no less satisfactory than the method of direct mixing. And we may go further. If a spontaneous flow of electrons is found, we can insert a certain opposing e.m.f. between the two electrodes, and see whether the spontaneous flow of electrons continues in the same direction in spite of this. If, for example, we insert a reverse e.m.f. of one volt between the electrodes, and find that the flow of electrons continues in the same direction as before, we can say that the occupied electronic level from which the electrons are coming must be more than one ϵ-volt higher than the vacant level to which they are going, or, if we are dealing with a more complicated case, we can draw an analogous quantitative conclusion.

If we measure the value of the opposing e.m.f. which is just sufficient to stop the flow of electrons from one species of ion to the other—if we measure the potential difference between the two electrodes—this is evidently the familiar process of measuring the e.m.f. of a cell; for the two vessels, coupled together in the way described, form, of course, a particular type of cell—a cell in which both electrodes are of an insoluble metal.

It may seem a very risky procedure to abandon the method of direct mixing, and to use instead such a roundabout method as that of the two separate half-cells coupled together. In such an indirect method there is room for various uncertainties, and there seems at first no guarantee that when we measure the p.d. between the electrodes we shall be determining the properties of the ions. If we are going to accept the results of this method as equally satisfactory, or more satisfactory than those obtained by direct mixing of the solutions, this can only be because we possess a sensitive check on the method, which enables us to reject all those cases where the method is impracticable. We have a sensitive test of this kind, which we can apply to any type of half-cell, namely the test of its "reversibility", which will be fully described in Chapter VIII.

We have seen how the flow of electrons along a wire may be a substitute for the direct transference of electrons from one species of ion to another by collision. We have so far been fixing attention on the electric current as a substitute for those collisions where an electron from one ion falls into a lower vacant level in the other. But in § 4 of the preceding chapter it was pointed out that the reverse type of collision also takes place; where a pair of ions have sufficient thermal energy an electron may be transferred back to a vacant level which is higher. The relative number of these reverse transfers depends on the relative concentration of the various substances and on the mean thermal energy of the ions. We must now notice that in the indirect method the wire between the electrodes is, so to say, completely unbiased, as between the forward and reverse direction, and provides an impartial substitute for both kinds of encounters. From this point of view, the spontaneous current which actually flows is the resultant of a tendency for electrons to flow in one direction and a smaller tendency for electrons to flow in the opposite direction; the relative magnitude in the two directions depends, as above, on the concentrations of the various species and on the thermal energy of the ions. The potential difference between the two electrodes depends on the relative concentrations of the various ions and on their thermal energy, that is to say, on the temperature.

In the investigation of the e.m.f. of cells during the last fifty years attention has been mainly devoted to elucidating the part played by the concentrations of the ions. In any half-cell a description of the concentration factor falls into two sections, which may be called primary and secondary. There is a primary effect common to all solutions, upon which is superposed a secondary factor describing the way in which the particular species of ions present differ from a perfect solute. Up to the present day, the unravelling of these concentration factors has so far monopolised attention that little or nothing has been done

to confront the more fundamental problem of interpreting the
absolute values of e.m.f.'s in terms of electronic and ionic
energies. In this book we discuss the working of cells only for
the sake of the light which such a study may throw upon the
nature of the ions concerned. From the observed values of
e.m.f.'s we wish to deduce and to check the values of such
quantities as J and W. We have to understand how the e.m.f.
depends upon the concentration, but only that we may eliminate
this factor.

In this discussion of e.m.f. we have so far had in view those
cells where both electrodes are acting merely as channels
through which electrons may flow. Of equal importance are
those cells where one or both electrodes are of a soluble metal,
and where, on passing a current, the electrode either dissolves
away or grows by deposition of positive cores. In the following
chapters, to distinguish these two kinds of metal electrode, we
shall for the sake of brevity use the terms "insoluble electrode"
and "soluble electrode"; it will always be understood that the
soluble electrode is dipping into a solution containing its own
ions. In the deposition and solution of any species of ion is
involved its characteristic energies, not only in solution but also
in aggregation with electrons to form solid metal. In a cell
containing two electrodes of this type we may, as before,
oppose the flow of electrons by introducing a reverse e.m.f. into
the external circuit of the cell; and the value of the e.m.f. which
we find is just sufficient to stop the flow of electrons gives us, as
before, information as to the energy of the ionic process.

If in both types of cell the electrode method is equivalent to
the method of direct mixing, and if the e.m.f. yields quantitative information, this can only be because the strengths of
the double layers which exist at the interfaces are such as to
give quantitative agreement—it can only be because the ionic
mechanisms are such as to cause each electrical double layer to
take up the appropriate strength. In the following chapters it
will be our aim to show quantitatively the mechanisms by
which this comes about.

When an electrode is dipping into a solution and has come to equilibrium, the strength of the electrical double layer has the same value over the whole surface of contact. If at any point the strength of the layer deviates momentarily from the value elsewhere, the ionic mechanism brings it back again immediately. If one takes a section through the metal electrode below the surface of the liquid, it is obvious that the double layer forms a complete envelope round the metal, as in fig. 26, and that no charge can pass out of the metal into the solution without

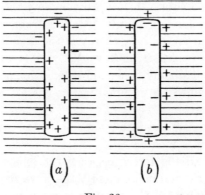

Fig. 26

passing through the envelope, which may be either positive inwards and negative outwards or else negative inwards and positive outwards. In the following chapters we shall use the symbol V to denote the strength of the double layer at any metal-liquid interface. We must clearly adopt a convention as to the sign of V. We shall choose to give V the same sign as the inner layer on the metal; when the layer is negative outwards and positive inwards V is a positive quantity, and vice versa. When V is negative the work to remove an electron from the metal is diminished, as in fig. 19d.

CHAPTER VII

§ 1. INTERIONIC FORCES

In connection with fig. 11 the conception of a lattice expanded n times uniformly in all directions was introduced. It was pointed out that if we imagine an ionic crystal to have been placed in a vacuum and then expanded to 1000 times its original volume, each ion being at rest, we still have about 1/10th of the lattice energy to supply before we complete the separation of the crystal into ions at infinite distances from each other. If, for example, the total lattice energy of the original crystal were 10 ϵ-volts per molecular unit, work equal to about 9 ϵ-volts would have been already done, and an additional 1 ϵ-volt would remain to do, since the residual lattice energy is proportional to $1/r$.

We may follow up this idea by imagining the expanded lattice to be situated in a medium of dielectric constant K, instead of in a vacuum. All the forces between the ions are reduced K times in strength, and consequently the work required to complete the separation of the ions (to large distances within the dielectric) will be K times less than the value considered above. The system will possess a small but definite residual lattice energy; in the numerical example cited, instead of 1 ϵ-volt, the value would be $1/K$ ϵ-volts, that is 1/80 ϵ-volt, if the dielectric were water at room temperature. If we wished to remove one of these ions from its position to a point within the dielectric at a great distance from the other ions, we should have to do a certain amount of work; if we wished to remove it to a long distance outside the dielectric, we should have to do this amount of work in addition to the usual solvation energy on crossing the boundary.

These ideas have been suggested here in order to enquire later how this imaginary system, with all its ions at rest in a lattice, would resemble and differ from a dilute solution containing the same species of ion, and the same number of ions per unit volume, dissolved in water or other solvent. We wish to know whether an ionic solution at room temperature possesses anything corresponding to the residual lattice energy of this imaginary expanded lattice. For if it does, the solvation energy of each of the ions will be greater than its solvation energy in pure solvent.

In Chapter I we examined the energy of a charge embedded in a dielectric medium, and compared it with the energy of the same charge *in vacuo*. We may now enquire whether the energy of an ion at rest in a solvent is modified by the presence of other positive and negative ions as they occur in a dilute solution. If so, the solvation energy of any ion will depend on the concentration of the solution.

When a charge q is at a distance r_1, from a similar charge, its potential energy in the field of this charge is q^2/Kr_1. When it is at a distance r_2 from an equal charge of opposite sign, its potential energy in the field of this charge is $-q^2/Kr_2$. Since potential energies are additive, its potential energy when both the other charges are present will be $q^2(1/r_1 - 1/r_2)/K$. If r_1 is the same as r_2, the bracketed expression vanishes and the potential energy of the ion will be the same as if both neighbours were absent. Now in a solution at room temperature the ions are all constantly moving from place to place. The nearest neighbours of any ion will be continually changing, and consequently its potential energy will be subject to rapid fluctuations. What we are concerned with is the time average of its potential energy. Any solution that is electrically neutral contains an equal quantity of positive and negative charge. For simplicity we shall discuss first a uni-univalent electrolyte, such as NaCl, in which the positive and negative ions are equal in number. The problem then resolves itself into the question whether the average distance r between like pairs of ions is the same as between unlike pairs.

In the dilute solution each solvated ion is being continually jostled by the surrounding solvent molecules, and consequently travels about with an ordinary Brownian movement. In this movement the route followed will to some extent at least be dictated by the electrostatic forces between the ions. The repulsion between ions of the same sign will oppose their approach, while the attraction between ions of opposite sign will encourage their approach. The result is that if we fix attention on any positive ion in solution, and observe its nearest ionic neighbours over a certain period of time, we shall find among them slightly more negatives than positives; while, if at the same time we fix attention on any negative ion, we shall find among its nearest neighbours more positives than negatives. We know that in the perfect order of a rock-salt crystal each positive ion is surrounded by six negatives and at the same time each negative by six positives; what we have here is a slight tendency towards such an orderly arrangement, or rather, towards that of the system suggested on p. 74 of this chapter, where we supposed the ions of an expanded lattice to be embedded in a dielectric medium. The state of any ionic solution is thus intermediate between a random distribution and a well-ordered distribution. We can either start from the random distribution, as we have done in this section, and show how the electrostatic forces introduce a certain amount of order, which is completely absent in any solution containing two species of *neutral* molecules. Or, alternatively, we may start with the expanded lattice of p. 74, whose lattice energy we know; and we can show how the Brownian movement destroys the lattice arrangement of the ions, without, however, reducing this energy to zero.

We see then the important fact that any solution possesses a small quasi-lattice energy due to the fact that the nearest neighbours of any ion contain more ions of unlike than of like sign. In any solution this energy belongs to the particular configuration of the ions in the same way that a lattice energy belongs to the ionic lattice of any crystal; and we shall call it the "configuration energy" of the solution.

Consider any ion in a dilute solution; to remove this ion from among its neighbours to a region of pure solvent a certain amount

of work will have to be done. If we wish to remove an ion from
a solution into a vacuum, this work must be done in addition
to the normal solvation energy for the ion in pure solvent. We
have then found the answer to our first question; the solvation
energy of an ion in a solution is slightly greater than for the
same ion in the pure solvent. By comparison with the numerical
example given on p. 74, we can see that the value of this increment
for the dilute solutions under discussion will be less than $1/100$
ϵ-volt. This is so small compared with the solvation energy
itself, that we have committed no serious error in speaking
hitherto of the value of W as if it were the same in a solution
as in pure solvent.

When we wish to take into account the small increment in W
we shall write

$$W = W_0 + \chi(c) \qquad \qquad \ldots\ldots(20),$$

where W_0 is the solvation energy characteristic of the ion in
pure solvent or infinitely dilute solution, and $\chi(c)$ is a quantity
which is zero when c is nearly zero. For many purposes it is
unnecessary to stress the difference between W and W_0. When
in § 3 we again consider the relation between W and Y we shall
at first disregard the distinction between W and W_0.

We wish to know how the configuration energy of a solution
depends on the concentration, on the dielectric constant of the
solvent, and on the charges borne by the ions. In Chapter XI we
shall solve this problem in detail for dilute solutions. Here we
may at least examine the principles involved.

Considering once more the expanded lattice of p. 74, it is clear
that, if for singly charged ions we substitute doubly charged
ions in the identical positions, this residual lattice energy will
take on a value four times as great, since all the electrostatic
forces are increased four times. And we may now notice the
important fact that this will be true, not only for a regular
lattice arrangement of ions, but for any given configuration at
all, provided that the ions are sufficiently far apart to exert
only electrostatic forces on each other. Whatever energy the
configuration possesses will vary as q^2. We shall have to decide

then whether, in a very dilute solution of a substance such as $CuSO_4$, the average relative positions of the ions is the same as in a solution of NaCl at the same concentration.

On p. 74 it was pointed out that if we imagine the expanded lattice to be immersed in various solvents with different values of K, its residual lattice energy in each solvent will be proportional to $1/K$. And we may now notice that this is so, not only for a regular periodic arrangement of the ions but for any configuration, provided that the forces are purely electrostatic, and that the configuration is the same in each solvent. Suppose then that we have certain species of ions dissolved in different solvents at the same small concentration. The question arises whether in these dilute solutions the average configuration of the ions is the same in the different solvents. If this were so, the configuration energy of the solutions would be proportional to $1/K$. For example, in a solvent with $K = 20$ the value would be four times as great as in water at room temperature.

In discussing the expanded lattice of p. 74, it was further pointed out that the energy is inversely proportional to the cube-root of the volume; if, for example, we reduce the volume to one-eighth, its lattice energy will be exactly doubled. If n is the number of ion pairs per unit volume, the energy varies as $\sqrt[3]{n}$. And we may now notice that this will be true from whatever arrangement of ions we start, provided that the geometrical configuration of the ions remains the same throughout—i.e. if the final state is a replica in miniature of the initial state. For use in later chapters we shall find it convenient to define a length

$$b = \frac{1}{\sqrt[3]{n}} \qquad \ldots\ldots(21).$$

Then, on changing the volume, all distances between ions will vary in proportion to b, and whatever energy the configuration possesses will vary as $1/b$, as in curve FG of fig. 11. We shall have to decide later whether in a solution at a certain concentration the average configuration of the particles is a replica of their configuration at all other concentrations. For a dilute solution containing only species of neutral molecules this certainly is so, all being merely random. If it were true for an ionic solution also, the quasi-lattice energy of the solution would be proportional to the cube-root of the concentration. We shall find, however, in Chapter XI that in dilute solutions it varies as the square-root of the concentration.

§ 2. OSMOTIC PRESSURE

In the foregoing paragraphs we have seen how a solution containing ions behaves differently from a solution containing only neutral particles. We may now briefly consider this difference in relation to the osmotic pressure of the solute. Suppose that the solution is contained in a cylinder whose piston is provided with a semi-permeable membrane—permeable to solvent but not to solute. When such a membrane separates a solution from pure solvent, the osmotic pressure arises from the fact that the solvent molecules striking the membrane on one side are fewer than the number striking on the other side. In what follows it is essential to consider what will happen when we diminish the volume v in which the solute is confined, by moving the piston downwards. Pure solvent flows through the membrane, but the solute particles behave in this process like a gas. To move the piston downwards isothermally we have to do work, that is, we have to supply energy. But this energy is not retained by the solution: it is given out as heat to the surroundings. The membrane in moving downwards causes the solute particles to rebound with greater kinetic energy than they otherwise would have had; this kinetic energy is given up to the solvent molecules, and thence to the surroundings. Conversely, in an isothermal expansion the solute particles give up energy to the piston; they receive more kinetic energy from the solvent molecules, which in turn derive the energy as heat from the surroundings.

It was found long ago that in dilute non-conducting solutions, the solute obeys the ordinary gas laws. All neutral substances, like sugar, at a given small molar concentration were found to exert the same pressure as a gas, namely that given by Boyle's law

$$P_0 = nkT \qquad \text{......(22)},$$

where k is Boltzmann's molecular gas constant, and n is the total number of molecules per cubic centimetre. A solution containing two or more species of molecules behaves like a mixture of gases; i.e. the total osmotic pressure depends only on the number of separate particles present, irrespective of their species.

In a compression the change in volume dv is a negative quantity; it is therefore more convenient to consider the work Pdv done by the system in an isothermal expansion, which will, of course, be equal to the work required for the reverse compression. Since $P_0 dv$ is equal to $nkT\,dv$, whatever amount of solute is under consideration, the work per molecule depends only on the ratio v_2/v_1 of the final to the initial volume, and is given by

$$\int_{v_1}^{v_2} \frac{kT}{v}\,dv = kT \log \frac{v_2}{v_1} = kT \log \frac{c_1}{c_2} \qquad \text{......(23)},$$

where c_1/c_2 is the ratio of the initial to the final concentration. This being the value of the work per molecule present, the work for any number N of molecules will be N times as large. In particular, for one mol of the solute we have to multiply by Avogadro's constant, giving just $RT \log \dfrac{c_1}{c_2}$.

For a solution containing positive and negative ions, however, the osmotic pressure cannot be obtained by inserting the total number of particles into (22). We have seen that the value of the configuration energy will certainly depend on the concentration in such a way that, if we diminish the volume occupied by the solute, the system falls to a state of lower electrostatic energy; we may picture this as going down a curve like GF of fig. 11. This means that the work required to compress the solute by a certain amount will be smaller than for a "perfect solute"—in fact, the $P_0 dv$ in (23) must be replaced by

$$P\,dv = P_0 dv - dF_e \qquad \text{......(24)},$$

where dF_e is the change in the electrostatic contribution to the free energy, which will be evaluated for dilute solutions in Chapter XI. We have then

$$P = P_0 - \frac{dF_e}{dv} \qquad \qquad \ldots\ldots(25).$$

In ionic solutions the expression (23) will hold within the experimental error only at exceptionally low concentrations, i.e. when c and c' are both exceedingly small, so that the interionic forces are negligible. If c_1 is large and only c_2 is small, the work done in an isothermal expansion will differ from (23) to some extent. We might say that the value is now $jRT \log \frac{c_1}{c_2}$, where j is a number differing somewhat from unity. It is more convenient, however, to put the number inside the logarithm, and to add a subscript to show that the value of the number depends on the value of c_1, but not in any detectable degree on c_2, provided that c_2 is below a certain limit; that is, the value of the work is written $RT \log \frac{f_1 c_1}{c_2}$; if neither c_1 nor c_2 is small, the work will be $RT \log \frac{f_1 c_1}{f_2 c_2}$. Numbers used in this way to indicate to what extent a solution differs from a perfect solution are called activity coefficients. The value depends on the particular species of ions present, but will always become indistinguishable from unity in sufficiently dilute solution. The relative activity a_1/a_2 of any component at two different concentrations is defined by

$$RT \log a_1/a_2 = F_1 - F_2 \qquad \qquad \ldots\ldots(26),$$

where F is the thermodynamic potential, or alternatively, the free energy; as the compressibility of liquids is so small, it is not usual to distinguish between these two quantities for dissolved substances. For the details of the various ways of defining activity coefficients, the reader is referred to the text-books on the subject.

In practice the concentrations are measured in mols per litre. When the concentration is exactly one mol per litre, the solute

is at unit concentration, but is not "at unit activity" except
when the activity coefficient f is equal to unity. A certain species
of ions will be at unit activity when the product fc is equal to
1·0 mol per litre. Take, for example, a solution where $c = 1·1$ mols
per litre; if the value of f at this concentration happens to be
just over 0·9, the substance will be at unit activity in this
solution.

§ 3. EQUILIBRIUM BETWEEN METALLIC IONS AND ELECTRODE

In the last section of Chapter IV we began to examine the
equilibrium at the surface of a soluble metal dipping into a
solution containing its own ions; but the problem was postponed
in order that a preliminary survey of ionic assemblies might
first be made; the study of the problem will be resumed here.
For each metal the work Y to remove a positive core from the
surface into a vacuum has a characteristic value, while the
solvation energy W depends also on the solvent used. We saw
that the work required to take a metallic core from the surface
into solution was $(Y - W)$. In drawing this conclusion we were
tacitly assuming that there was no electrical double layer at the
interface between the metal and the solution. We saw, however,
in Chapter IV, that when a soluble metal is dipped into a solvent,
or into a solution containing its own ions, an electrical double
layer always arises at the interface. When such a double layer
is present, the amount of work to take a core into solution will
be greater or less according to the sign of the double layer. If
the ion bears a charge $m\epsilon$, the work required to take it through a
double layer of strength V is $\pm m\epsilon V$. Hence the work required to
remove it from the surface into solution is now $(Y - W - m\epsilon V)$,
according to the convention of p. 73.

The next step must be to modify fig. 20 to represent the
situation where a double layer is present. The required modifica-
tion is to be made in exactly the same way as in fig. 14; that
is to say, the initial curve must be compounded with a curve
contributed by the double layer. Supposing, as usual, that the

metal is at the left of the diagram, if the double layer is positive outwards, we shall have to add the ordinates of a curve like curve b of fig. 14 to the initial curve, the step-up in curve b being equal to $m\epsilon V$. The effect is to raise the potential valley on the right with respect to that on the left by this amount, as in fig. 27a. If, on the other hand, the double layer is positive inwards, the effect will be to depress the valley on the right with respect to that on the left.

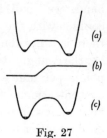

Fig. 27

In the case of electrons, we saw in fig. 14 how the raising of one potential box relative to the other checked the flow from left to right until equilibrium came about. The same thing will happen here with positive ions. The electrical double layer which grows up equalises the ionic transitions in the two directions, so that equilibrium comes about spontaneously. We may begin now to enquire how the conditions may be expressed quantitatively.

If we consider any face of a metallic crystal, we find the metallic cores in a regular arrangement; the number of these cores per unit area of the surface will depend upon the particular crystal faces. In any micro-crystalline piece of metal, however, all the crystal faces will be represented. We need not take into account different faces, but need consider only a plane surface with N metallic cores per unit area, where N is characteristic of the metal in its micro-crystalline state.

Suppose now that the piece of metal is dipped into a dilute solution containing its own ions at a certain concentration. If we look at the surface of the metal at any moment, we can divide these N lattice points into two classes. At most of these points solvent molecules will be found in contact with the metal; at each of these points there is a probability of the metallic core becoming detached from the surface by the process of fig. 21. A transition in which an ion passes into solution may, for brevity, be called an s-transition, and the initial situation which gives rise to this transition may be called an s-situation. (The corresponding quantities for deposition will be called d-transitions and d-situations.) The total number of s-situations is equal to the number of lattice points in contact with which are solvent molecules. At a few of the lattice points, on the other hand, we shall find solvated metallic ions momentarily in contact with the surface of the metal; at each of these points there is a possibility of the ion being deposited on the surface, i.e. the configuration is a d-situation. The number of such lattice points per unit area of the electrode depends directly on the concentration of the solution. If the solution is dilute they will be very few in number compared with the former; the number of d-situations will be small compared with the number of s-situations. To compensate for this difference the energy of the base of one potential valley must be brought to a certain position relative to the energy of the other. The important point to be made clear is that for a given concentration of a solution this relative position at equilibrium does not depend on the relative values of W and Y.

From the discussion in Chapter IV it appeared possible that for some solvated metallic ions W is greater than Y, as in fig. 27a, while for others W is less than Y. Later, in Chapter XIV, we shall have to enquire whether both types of ion exist in nature; but for the present we shall waive this question. We can imagine a simple case in which W happens to be exactly equal to Y. Of the three cases we will discuss this one first.

(1) W is equal to Y. Initially the d-transitions and s-transitions are on the same footing. And since the number of s-situations is far greater, more ions go into solution than are deposited. The electrical double layer which grows up is negative inwards, and raises the potential valley in solution with respect to that on the surface of the metal (as in fig. 27c). The s-transitions are checked, and the double layer grows until the number of s-transitions per second is as small as the number of d-transitions. At room temperature the magnitude of the double layer required to cut down the number of s-transitions will in this case be very small, because by the Boltzmann Law nearly all the

ions are in their lowest vibrational level. As soon as the lowest levels are put out of action the number of transitions is enormously reduced, and a small fraction of an ϵ-volt may, therefore, suffice. We conclude then that when $W = Y$ a weak double layer on the metal is required, negative inwards and of this magnitude.

(2) When W is greater than Y, the process is similar. For a given concentration the potential valley on the right must be raised to an energy lying above that on the left by the same amount as in case (1). The strength of the double layer needed to do this is obviously greater than before by an amount $(W - Y)$.

(3) When W is considerably less than Y, the situation is reversed. The potential valley on the right is initially too far above that on the left, and must be lowered. This comes about automatically, because it is at first almost impossible for positive cores to leave the metal surface; the number of ions being deposited from solution will be greater than the number going into solution. In this way an electrical double layer will grow up which has the opposite sign from that in cases (1) and (2); it is positive inwards.

§ 4. THE STRENGTH OF THE DOUBLE LAYER

To obtain an expression for V, at any temperature T, we have to take into account the thermal energy of the ions. As explained in § 3 of Chapter v, this will involve taking into account their concentration. Let the ratio of the number of metallic ions to the number of solvent molecules be defined as the concentration c in theoretical units.

Even at room temperature some ions are in high vibration levels. Speaking first of the ions on the surface of the lattice, the fraction of the total number that are in a level of energy U will be given by an expression containing the factor $\exp\{(U_m - U)/kT\}$, where U_m is the energy of the lowest quantum level of a metallic surface ion. For the ions in solution the distribution will involve a similar factor $\exp\{(U_s - U)/kT\}$, where U_s is the energy of the lowest level of a solvated ion. We have then two Boltzmann distributions, and our problem is to work out the equilibrium between them. This is, in fact, what has to be done in describing the equilibrium at any type of electrode. Although in this chapter we are considering one particular type of electrode, the expressions which we shall deduce are immediately adaptable to other types.

In the symbols U_m and U_s we are, of course, referring to the same lowest levels which determine the quantities Y and W. Whereas hitherto we have used Y or W to reckon downwards the depth of the level below the energy of a free ion, here it is more convenient to use positive energies

$$U_m - U_s = -(Y - W) \qquad \text{......(27)}.$$

In the absence of an electrical double layer the energy difference between the lowest level on either side is given by (27). When a double layer of strength V is present, one set of levels becomes shifted with respect to the other by an amount $n\epsilon V$, where $n\epsilon$ is the charge borne by the ion in question. If we retain U_s to denote the energy of the lowest level in solution, the energy of the lowest level on the surface is now $U_m + n\epsilon V$, following the convention adopted at the end of Chapter VI as to the sign of V.

The simpler the treatment, the more easily can the mechanism of the equilibrium be visualised. The expression for V obtained below by treating the vibrational levels as one-dimensional has the same form as that given by a general treatment using the methods of statistical mechanics. Of the total number of lattice ions per unit area of the surface a fraction,

$$F(U)\, dU = \frac{1}{kT} \exp\,(U_m + n\epsilon V - U)/kT\, dU \quad \text{......(28)},$$

will be in levels between U and $U + dU$, all values of U being possible between $(U_m + n\epsilon V)$ and infinity. The number of d-situations per unit area is proportional to the number of ions in solution, while the number of s-situations is proportional to the number of solvent molecules in the solution. Thus, if the number of s-situations associated with the energy U is $N_s F(U)\, dU$, the number of d-situations associated with the same energy U will be

$$\frac{N}{kT} \exp (U_s - U)/kT \, dU \qquad \ldots\ldots(29),$$

where $N/N_s = c$.

For equilibrium the number of d-situations multiplied by the probability of a d-transition must be equal to the number of s-situations multiplied by the probability of an s-transition. If the two probabilities are not equal, let the ratio of the latter probability to the former be β, a factor not far from unity and independent of the concentration. Then detailed balancing requires that

$$N_s \exp (U_m + n\epsilon V - U)/kT = \beta N \exp (U_s - U)/kT \quad \ldots\ldots(30).$$

That is to say

$$\beta c = \exp (n\epsilon V + U_m - U_s)/kT \qquad \ldots\ldots(31).$$

Hence the strength of the electrical double layer at any temperature T is given by

$$V = \frac{U_s - U_m}{n\epsilon} + \frac{kT}{n\epsilon} \log \beta c \qquad \ldots\ldots(32).$$

In deriving (32) we have been taking the solvation energy of the ion to be independent of the concentration of the solution. Even in dilute solution we should use (20), which may be put in the form

$$U_s = U_s{}^0 - \chi(c) \qquad \ldots\ldots(33).$$

When this is substituted in (32) we have

$$V = \frac{U_s{}^0 - U_m}{n\epsilon} + \frac{kT}{n\epsilon} \left(\log \beta c - \frac{\chi(c)}{kT} \right) \quad \ldots\ldots(34).$$

The first term is equal to $(Y - W_0)/n\epsilon$; and by a change of notation the terms involving c may be united. If we define a function ζ by $kT \log \zeta(c) = -\chi(c)$, we obtain

$$V = \frac{Y - W_0}{n\epsilon} + \frac{kT}{n\epsilon} \log fc \qquad \ldots\ldots(35),$$

where f, equal to $\zeta\beta$, is evidently an activity coefficient. As the first term is independent of the concentration of the solution, (35) is of the form

$$V = V_0 + \frac{RT}{nF} \log a \qquad \ldots\ldots(36).$$

The sign of the double layer given by (35) is the same as that deduced from fig. 27. As defined, fc is always less than unity and $\log fc$ is a negative quantity. We see then that when W is equal to or greater than Y (i.e. when U_s is equal to or less than U_m), the double layer will be negative inwards; and the weaker the solution, the more negative will it become. The lower the temperature the less important is the thermal energy of the ions, and the more nearly will $n\epsilon V$ approach the value $Y - W_0$.

In the last paragraph of Chapter v, in discussing ions from a different point of view, we noticed a condition which must be satisfied for equilibrium at any metal electrode. It can be shown that for every soluble metal, when the strength of the double layer has the value given by (35), this other condition is certainly satisfied at the same time.

CHAPTER VIII

§ 1. CELLS AND HALF-CELLS

In Chapter VI a little was said about the electromotive force of cells. In this chapter we shall begin to treat this subject in detail. Before attempting any analysis it will be better to approach the subject from the experimental point of view, to consider how e.m.f.'s are measured, and what conventions are usually adopted in tabulating the observed values.

Every simple cell consists of two half-cells. In the Daniell cell one half-cell contains a piece of copper dipping into a solution of copper sulphate, while the other half-cell contains a piece of zinc dipping into a solution of zinc sulphate. In any cell the two half-cells, which may be called A and B, act quite independently of each other. In one half-cell the electrode may be of a soluble metal, and in the other half-cell of an insoluble metal. A cell may be formed by coupling together one half-cell with another half-cell of any type; the only restriction is that the two solutions must be such that when put into contact they undergo no chemical interaction. In general any piece of metal dipping into any conducting solution may be regarded as a half-cell.

The essential property of a cell is that when the liquid parts of the two half-cells are put into contact either through a narrow tube or a porous partition, etc., the pieces of metal A and B are found to be at different potentials, so that if they are connected by means of an electrical conductor, a spontaneous current is found to flow through the latter. In the interior of the cell the same current is being carried by the motion of ions.

To measure the characteristic e.m.f. of a cell we introduce, by means of a potentiometer, an opposing e.m.f. into the external circuit. When the value of this applied e.m.f. is raised until it becomes nearly equal to the e.m.f. in the cell, the current that is being drawn from the cell becomes very small. If the value of

the applied e.m.f. is further increased, the current can be made
to fall to zero, and thus the value of the e.m.f. of this particular
cell can be determined. In some types of cell, of which the
Daniell cell is an example, if the applied opposing e.m.f. is now
slightly increased, a current begins to flow through the cell in
the opposite direction, the value of this current being proportional to the small increment that has been made in the applied
e.m.f. Under these circumstances it is found that the processes
in each half-cell, which formerly accompanied the flow of current, are now simply taking place in the reverse direction. Such
a cell is called a reversible cell—meaning reversible both in its
mechanism and in the thermodynamic sense.

From what has been said, it is clear that in measuring the
e.m.f. of a cell we are interested in its condition when no current
is flowing, or when a very small current is flowing. Since the
resistance of the electrolyte is not more than a few ohms, the
total ohmic drop of potential in the liquid, when a current of
one microampere is flowing, will not be more than a few mil-
lionths of a volt, and may be neglected. The ohmic drop in the
metal electrodes will be smaller still.

Some cells used in practice contain a saturated solution in
contact with some of the substance in solid form. In this volume
we shall confine attention to the simpler cells, in which no solid
is present other than the metal electrodes. Each simple half-cell,
then, consists of two conductors, one metallic and the other
electrolytic. There is no appreciable p.d. inside the conductors,
but there are double layers at the junctions between them. Of
these the potential difference at the junction between the two
liquids is in practice always a small fraction of a volt (the same
solvent being used in each half-cell), and by various devices
can be reduced to zero or almost to zero. In discussing the e.m.f.
of a cell, unless the p.d. at the liquid-liquid junction is specially
mentioned, it is assumed that it has been eliminated. We are
left then with three surfaces of contact—the two solid-liquid
interfaces and the one metal-metal junction which we obtain
when we close the external circuit of the cell. There may be an

electrical double layer at each of these contacts. But when the electrodes in the two half-cells are of the same metal, there will be no electrical double layer in the external circuit when we make contact. There is, thus, an important distinction between cells in which both electrodes are of the same metal, and cells where the two electrodes are of different metals, as in the Daniell cell. In those of the former class, which may be called isometallic cells, we are left only with the electrical double layer at the solid-liquid interface in each half-cell. To avoid using a long expression to describe the surface of contact between the electrode and the solution we shall call it simply "the interface". Further, the term isometallic is to be taken to refer only to the material of the electrodes and not to the species of metallic ions which may be present in the solutions.

§ 2. TEST OF REVERSIBILITY

The difference in the behaviour of a reversible and an irreversible cell was mentioned above. Suppose that in the exterior circuit of the cell we insert a small opposing e.m.f., whose value we raise until successively (1) the current being drawn from the cell falls to a very small value, (2) the current becomes imperceptible, and (3) a very small current begins to flow in the reverse direction. If the difference of potential between the terminals of the cell remains at almost the same value from (1) to (3), this is a reversible cell. But in an irreversible cell the necessary increment in the opposing e.m.f. is considerable.

When a cell behaves reversibly, we know that both half-cells are reversible; either of these will behave reversibly no matter with what other half-cell it is coupled. When a cell does not behave reversibly we do not at first know whether this behaviour is due to either of the half-cells or to both, but we can find out, by coupling each in turn to a half-cell which we already know to be reversible.

Suppose we take three half-cells of different kinds, A, B, and C, and put their solutions in contact, as in fig. 28. Fixing

attention on the half-cells containing electrodes A and B, we see
that they together form a cell AB, whose properties are the
same whether C is present or not, pro-
vided that we ensure that no current
flows through C. In the same way if
we fix attention on the half-cells A
and C, the properties of the cell AC
are the same whether B is present or
not, so long as no current flows
through B. And the same is true for

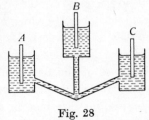

Fig. 28

the half-cells B and C, so long as no current flows through A.

If one of these half-cells is already known to be reversible, this
arrangement may be used to test experimentally whether each
of the other half-cells is reversible or not. Suppose that C is
known to be a reversible half-cell. By taking an external variable source of e.m.f. and connecting it to the electrodes A and B,
we can cause a small steady current to flow through the cell AB
either in the direction A to B or in the direction B to A at will.
And we can proceed meanwhile to measure the potential difference between A and C under three conditions: (1) when the
electrode B is insulated, (2) when a small, steady current, say a
microampere, is flowing through AB in the direction A to B, and
(3) when the same steady current is flowing in the direction
B to A. If the potential difference between A and C is not the
same under these three conditions, this must be due to a change
in the strength of the double layer at the interface between the
electrode A and the solution. If an appreciable change in the
p.d. is found, this cannot be due to any change at the interface
of C, since C is known to be a reversible half-cell. And, with so
small a current flowing, the ohmic drop in the solution between
A and B must be extremely small. Any change in the p.d.
between A and C greater than this must be due to a change in
the strength of the electrical double layer at the solid-liquid
interface in the half-cell A. In fact, the observed change in this
p.d. is an exact measure of the sign and magnitude of the change
in the double layer inside the half-cell A. If no appreciable

alteration is observed, A is a reversible half-cell as well as C. In the same way we can next measure the p.d. between the terminals of B and C under three conditions; when the terminal of A is insulated, and when a small current is flowing through AB in either direction. Any change in the measured p.d. will be just the change in the electrical double layer inside the half-cell B.

§ 3. THE MECHANISM OF REVERSIBILITY

We may next ask what are the implications of reversibility in any half-cell from the point of view of atomic mechanism. We can at once answer that reversibility implies that the half-cell contains a certain amount of some substance in each of two states which differ in some way electrically. In one state, or both, the particles of this substance are positive or negative ions. When a current flows, an equivalent amount of the substance changes over from one state to the other. In the external circuit and in the metallic electrodes the current is carried by electrons, and in the solution by ions. When one electron (or one pair of electrons, and so on) has passed round the external circuit, in each half-cell an ion has been either formed or discharged, or it has had its degree of ionisation raised or lowered—at any rate we may say that a positive or negative ion has passed from a certain initial state to a certain final state. If we reverse the direction of the current, an ion passes back to the initial state. In every half-cell we then recognise the existence of two states which we may call state 1 and state 2. Every reversible half-cell must contain an appreciable amount of substance in each of these conjugate states; there must be some in state 1 ready to change over to state 2 if we pass a current in the appropriate direction, and some in state 2 ready to change over to state 1 if we choose to pass a current in the reverse direction. Let the concentration of the substance in state 1 be denoted by c_1 and the concentration in state 2 by c_2.

If we couple up a half-cell with various other half-cells in turn, it will in some cases provide the positive terminal, and in other cases the negative terminal of the cell. We must define states 1 and 2 in each half-cell in a way which is independent of the particular half-cell to which it is coupled. Let us then define these states in such a way that, when electrons are flowing *from* the external circuit through the terminal into the electrode of this half-cell, material in the half-cell is changing from 1 to 2. Then in any complete cell when one half-cell is changing from 1 to 2, the other is changing from 2 to 1, the positive terminal of the cell being provided by the former and the negative terminal by the latter.

In most simple types of half-cell the substance is in solution in both the states 1 and 2; and c_1 and c_2 denote the concentrations of the solutes. The type of half-cell containing a soluble electrode discussed in the preceding chapter is, however, an exception. In state 1 the metallic ions are in solution at a concentration c_1; and in state 2 the ions are incorporated into the electrode as cores of the lattice. In the lattice the number of cores per unit volume is a fixed characteristic of the material, and is not under our control. Half-cells containing soluble electrodes are peculiar in this respect. In other types of half-cell the concentrations of the substance in both states 1 and 2 can be chosen at will, within the limits set by the solubility of the substance.

As mentioned above, no appreciable change in the strength of the double layer occurs when the direction of the current through a reversible half-cell is reversed, provided that the current density is small. The reason for this is clear. Even when no current is flowing, particles at the surface of the electrode are all the time changing from state 1 to state 2 and from state 2 to state 1. The number changing from 1 to 2 per second is, in fact, exactly equal to the number changing from 2 to 1. There is an electrical double layer at the interface whose strength has the particular value which makes these numbers equal. An extremely small change in the strength of this double layer is sufficient to upset this balance. Hence we can cause a perceptible current to flow in either direction without an appreciable change in the value of the double layer at the interface.

§ 4. EQUILIBRIUM BETWEEN NEGATIVE
IONS AND AN ELECTRODE

When a cell is generating a current, or when some external e.m.f. is sending a steady current through the cell, the solutions in the cell must of course remain electrically neutral. That is to say, if a certain number of positive charges are passing into solution at one electrode, either an equal number of positive charges must be removed from the solution at the other electrode, or else an equal number of *negative* charges must be sent into the solution. If we couple together two half-cells of the kind described in the preceding chapter, the cell is of the former class— while positive ions go into solution from one electrode, an equivalent number of positive ions are deposited on the other electrode, and the total number of negative ions in solution remains constant.

In order that a metal electrode may be dissolving as positive ions, an equivalent stream of electrons must be flowing at the same time from the electrode into the external circuit, to prevent the accumulation of charge in the metal. In order that a stream of *negative* ions may be formed at the electrode of a cell, a steady stream of electrons must be flowing into it from the external circuit. If solid iodine were a conductor of electricity, we could imagine ourselves using a crystal of iodine in contact with a suitable solvent to provide (and to discharge) negative iodine ions, just as we use a crystal of silver to provide positive silver ions. In the same way, if liquid bromine were a conductor, we could imagine ourselves using a pool of bromine in contact with a solvent or with a solution of a bromide, to provide and to discharge negative bromine ions, just as we use a pool of mercury to provide mercury positive ions. Unfortunately elements such as iodine and bromine, which form negative ions in solution, are insulators, and the necessary stream of electrons will not flow through them. Accordingly, in order to form or to discharge negative ions, it is necessary to provide an ancillary conductor to carry the stream of electrons from or into the external circuit.

For this purpose one uses a piece of metal dipping into the solution. Since this metal should play no part in the process, other than acting as a channel for the electrons, one uses a metal which is insoluble and is not easily oxidised, such as platinum or iridium.

The kind of half-cell in which we shall be interested is one in which the transformation of negative ions into neutral substance, and of neutral substance into negative ions, takes place equally readily in either direction. The piece of metal will be dipping into a mixed solution, in which both negative ions and neutral substance are dissolved. Such an arrangement forms a reversible half-cell, which may be coupled with any other half-cell. According to our definition the neutral substance represents state 1, and the negative ions state 2. The negative ions at concentration c_2 are, of course, accompanied by an equivalent number of positive ions. When a current flows these positive ions remain in solution unchanged. It is found that at low concentrations the behaviour of the half-cell is independent of the particular species of positive ion present.

Although cells of this type were investigated before the end of the last century, a description of them is omitted from many text-books. As they are of considerable theoretical interest, it is worth while giving a brief sketch of one such investigation. Küster and Crotogino* in 1899 studied a series of half-cells, all containing in aqueous solution the same concentration of neutral iodine but widely different concentrations of potassium iodide. These half-cells being coupled in turn to a standard half-cell, the e.m.f.'s of the resultant cells were measured and compared at constant temperature. It was found that, the greater the concentration of the potassium iodide, the more negative did the terminal of the iodine half-cell become relative to the terminal of the standard half-cell. This behaviour is to be expected if the positive ions play no part in determining the strength of the double layer. The concentration of the potassium iodide being varied by a factor of 1200, it was found that over

* *Zeit. f. anorg. Chem.* **23**, 87 (1899).

this range the e.m.f.'s of the cells could be represented very nearly by the simple expression

$$\mathscr{E} = \mathscr{E}_0 - 0.06 \log_{10} c \qquad \ldots\ldots(37).$$

The value of the constant $\mathscr{E}_0$ depended, of course, on the particular kind of half-cell to which the iodine half-cells were coupled. In this solution there is a certain complication due to the formation of triatomic ions I_3^-.

A study was also made of a series of half-cells, all containing the same concentration of potassium iodide but varying amounts of neutral iodine in aqueous solution. It was found that when the concentration of the neutral iodine was increased, this caused a change in the potential of the electrode in the opposite direction to the former; i.e. the electrode became progressively more positive with respect to the solution. This behaviour of the electrical double layer is again what we should expect from the ionic mechanism.

Similar behaviour has been found in half-cells containing bromine ions and neutral bromine in solution.

§ 5. THE FERRIC-FERROUS HALF-CELL

We will pass on now to another type of half-cell, where an insoluble electrode is dipping into a mixed solution, but one which contains a species of metallic ion in two stages of ionisation. If a piece of platinum, or other insoluble metal, is dipping into a mixed solution of ferric and ferrous salts dissolved in water, pyridine, or other solvent, such an arrangement forms a half-cell, which may be coupled with any other reversible half-cell to form a reversible cell. It will be convenient to suppose that one and the same species of negative ion is present in both half-cells—say chlorine ions.

By introducing a variable e.m.f. into the external circuit, a current of any desired magnitude may be caused to flow through the cell either in one direction or the other. Since the two half-cells act quite independently, we may first confine our attention to the ferric-ferrous half-cell.

When the external e.m.f. is driving electrons into the platinum, these electrons flow from the platinum into the solution. The electrons are, in fact, passing to the Fe^{+++} ions, for it is found that an equivalent number of Fe^{+++} ions are being converted to Fe^{++}. Conversely, when the current is flowing through the platinum in the opposite direction, electrons are passing from the solution into the platinum; the electrons are, in fact, coming from the Fe^{++} of which an equivalent number are changing into Fe^{+++}. Thus, the platinum electrode is used either to extract electrons from the solution or to pump electrons into it (the electrical neutrality of the solution being maintained by the passage of negative ions across the liquid boundary between the two half-cells).

Let R be the ratio between the number of chlorine ions and the total number of Fe ions present in the half-cell at any moment. If at the beginning the solution is mainly ferric, the value of R will be near 3. As we pump electrons through the platinum into the solution, changing Fe^{+++} into Fe^{++}, the value of R falls, passing through 2·9, 2·8, ... and so on. When the value of R approaches 2, the solution is nearly all ferrous. The question arises: can the process be continued to make the value of R fall below 2, changing Fe^{++} ions to Fe^{+}; and if not, why not? At the same time we may ask whether a similar experiment can be made with ions of other elements, for example to change Al^{+++} ions to Al^{++}. Before these questions can be answered in detail there are many problems to be considered. In the next chapter we begin by examining the status of multiply charged ions in solution.

CHAPTER IX

§ 1. SUCCESSIVE DEGREES OF IONISATION

When the temperature of a metallic vapour, such as calcium vapour, is raised sufficiently, thermal ionisation sets in. Electrons become free, leaving singly charged calcium ions, Ca^+. In the atmosphere of the sun, for example, the temperature is sufficiently high to ionise the calcium vapour almost completely to Ca^+; but the amount of Ca^{++} in equilibrium with this is extremely small. This result is to be expected. To remove another electron from the ion Ca^+ requires a further 11·8 ϵ-volts; and, inserting this quantity into the Boltzmann factor, we find that the relative amount of Ca^{++} in equilibrium with Ca^+ is very small, until an exceedingly high temperature is reached. The valency of calcium in its chemical compounds is 2, but this is irrelevant; only one of the valence electrons becomes free.

If one were to ask why Ca^{++} and Al^{+++} ions are known in solution, while Ca^+, Al^{++}, and Al^+ are unknown, the usual reply would be that calcium is divalent, and aluminium is trivalent. But the rules of chemical combination describe how atoms and ions combine to form molecules and aggregates. In dilute solution the positive and negative ions are as separate as in a vapour, and the rules of valency can have no direct bearing on the problem. It is true of course, that, if the only way of obtaining calcium ions in solution were to dissolve a substance containing divalent calcium, we should never obtain anything but Ca^{++}. But although in the experiment with ferric ions, described at the end of the previous chapter, the value of R was initially 3, we were able to make R fall continuously through fractional values; and the charge on the Fe ions was not limited by the particular compound which had been dissolved at the beginning. If a similar experiment cannot be performed starting with Al^{+++} ions, i.e. if the Al^{+++} ion cannot be induced to take up an electron, this can certainly not be ascribed to the nonexistence of solid $AlCl_2$. Where a limitation on ions in solution exists, this must be described entirely in terms of solvent and solvated ions.

The questions raised here seem never to have received much attention; and it is easy to see why at no period in the history of physical chemistry they have been felt to present an acute problem. For in the early days electrolytes in solution were thought to consist of neutral molecules, which were temporarily broken down to some extent into ions on the application of an electric field. When it was first suggested that in dilute solution the separation into ions might be a permanent state, the idea met with considerable opposition. Its adoption took place so gradually that usually ions in dilute solution are still thought of as parts of a molecule rather than as independent particles, like ions in a gas.

The methods of solving these problems will be given in Chapter xv. In this chapter we shall begin by studying in general the nature and behaviour of multiply charged ions in solution. We shall approach the question by the method adopted in the preceding chapters for singly charged ions—that is, we shall discuss first atomic ions *in vacuo*, then molecular ions, and then, by a simple transition, ions in solution.

§ 2. ELECTRONIC LEVELS OF IONS *IN VACUO*

In Chapter v we have considered how a positive ion *in vacuo* may capture an electron by collision with a neutral atom of some other element. A doubly charged ion may capture an electron, not only from a neutral atom in the same way, but, under certain circumstances, it may also capture an electron from a singly charged positive ion; it may clearly do this when the occupied electronic level of the latter lies higher than the vacant level of the former. Hitherto in discussing the electronic levels of positive ions we have only been concerned with the vacant level of the ion (and throughout the book when we say *the* vacant level we shall mean the normal lowest level into which an electron can be captured). But we have just seen that sometimes the level in which we are interested will not be the vacant level but the occupied level of the positive ion (and when we say *the* occupied level we mean the highest level of the ion from which an electron can be removed).

In the hydrogen ion, H^+, the depth of the vacant level is 13·53 ϵ-volts, and the ion possesses no occupied level. We see from Table XI that in the ion He^+ the depth of the vacant level is 24·47 ϵ-volts, and there is also a deep occupied level at 54·16 ϵ-volts. The doubly charged ion He^{++} has a vacant level which, of course, lies at the same value, namely 54·16 ϵ-volts; the energy liberated when He^{++} captures an electron is the same as the work required to remove an electron from He^+. This identity applies to any element in two successive stages of ionisation, m and $(m+1)$. The depth of the occupied electronic level of the ion bearing a charge $m\epsilon$ is, by definition, the same as the depth of the vacant level in the ion bearing the charge $(m+1)\epsilon$; they are merely two aspects of the same quantity.

Suppose now, to take an example, we wish to know whether the calcium ion Ca^{++} could capture an electron from a singly charged titanium ion Ti^+; we see from Table XI that the ion Ti^+ possesses an occupied level whose depth is 13·6 ϵ-volts. The Ca^+ ion has an occupied level at a depth 11·82 ϵ-volts—or in other words the Ca^{++} ion has a vacant level at 11·82 ϵ-volts. This vacant level is nearly 2 ϵ-volts higher than the occupied level of Ti^+. If then a Ca^{++} ion collided with a Ti^+ ion, *in vacuo*, it would not capture an electron from the latter, even if their relative velocity were high enough to enable them to approach sufficiently close.

It is not then the pair of ions Ca^{++} and Ti^+ that are of interest, but the alternative pair Ca^+ and Ti^{++}. For the data which we have just quoted are equivalent to the statement that the vacant level in Ti^{++} is nearly two ϵ-volts lower than the occupied level in Ca^+. It is obviously a simple matter to draw up a list of the elements in the order of the electronic levels of their ions *in vacuo*. And we may pass on now to molecular ions.

§ 3. IONISATION POTENTIALS OF MOLECULAR IONS

If we start with an atomic negative ion A^- and remove successive electrons we obtain in turn a neutral atom, an ion A^+, an ion A^{++}, and so on, as in fig. 5. But, as pointed out in Chapter II, in the case of molecular ions we are more restricted as to types, because some of the successive stages may be unstable. It will, however, be convenient to consider a case where all successive types exist, although the case may be an imaginary one. Suppose then that two atoms A and B form not only a neutral diatomic molecule AB, but also a negative ion $(AB)^-$, and positive ion $(AB)^+$, and $(AB)^{++}$. In fig. 8 we have already considered AB and $(AB)^+$, and have shown how their relation to each other may be expressed by means of two curves. These two curves reappear in the middle of fig. 29. Above them has been added a curve for $(AB)^{++}$, and

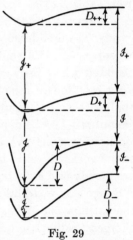

Fig. 29

below them another curve for $(AB)^-$. Let D_- and $\mathscr{J}_-$ denote the dissociation energy and ionisation potential of the negative ion, and so on.

The ion $(AB)^+$ possesses a vacant electron level; the depth of the level is equal to $\mathscr{J}$, whose value according to (9) is given by

$$\mathscr{J} = \mathscr{I} - D_+ + D \qquad \ldots\ldots(38).$$

We can obtain a set of expressions of this kind. The supernumerary electron in the ion $(AB)^-$ is in a level whose depth is $\mathscr{J}_-$. From fig. 29 its value is clearly given by

$$\mathscr{J}_- = \mathscr{I}_- + D_- - D \qquad \ldots\ldots(39).$$

The ion $(AB)^{++}$ has a vacant level whose depth is $\mathscr{J}_+$ given by

$$\mathscr{J}_+ = \mathscr{I}_+ - D_{++} + D_+ \qquad \ldots\ldots(40),$$

and so on for the higher degrees of ionisation.

§ 4. IONISATION POTENTIALS IN SOLUTION

Passing on now to ions in solution, it will be our object to make a similar study of their electron levels, to obtain a set of expressions like (39) and (40), and a diagram corresponding to fig. 29. We have already seen in fig. 10 how the solvation energy of an ion corresponds to the dissociation potential of a molecular ion; the depth of the minimum of the curve, instead of D or D_-, is for a singly charged ion W or W_-. In the same way, corresponding to D_+ and D_{++}, we shall for doubly and trebly charged ions have other quantities; we have seen in Chapter I that we must expect the solvation energy for these to be four and nine times that of a singly charged ion of the same radius.

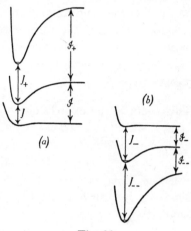

Fig. 30

For any ionic species which occurs in solution in two or more stages of ionisation, like Fe^{++} and Fe^{+++}, we shall have a family of curves like those of fig. 29. The resemblance will be close except for one of the curves, namely the one corresponding to the curve for the neutral molecule. There will be little or no attraction between solvent molecules and a neutral atom; this particular potential energy will, therefore, have only a shallow minimum, if any at all. For an element which furnishes positive ions in solution we thus have fig. 30a, the lowest curve being for the neutral atom. Fig. 30b is for an element which furnishes negative ions, the upper curve being for the neutral atom. We may deal with the latter first. The supernumerary electron in the singly charged negative ion is in a level at a depth given by J_-, corresponding to $\mathcal{J}_-$ in fig. 29. It is clear from the diagram that, if the upper curve is sufficiently flat, the term corresponding to D in expression (39) drops out, leaving only two terms on the right-hand side. The vertical distance between the two upper curves of fig. 30b is thus given by

$$J_- = \mathscr{I}_- + W_- \qquad \ldots\ldots(41).$$

But this is just the expression that was deduced in Chapter v by a different method.

Turning next to an element furnishing positive ions, in fig. 30a the singly charged solvated ion possesses a vacant level at a depth J, corresponding to $\mathscr{I}$ in fig. 29. Again, if the lower curve is sufficiently flat, the term corresponding to the last term in expression (38) drops out, leaving only two terms on the right-hand side. The vertical distance denoted by J in fig. 30a is clearly given by

$$J = \mathscr{I} - W \qquad \ldots\ldots(42).$$

This again is the expression which was deduced in Chapter v. If one looks at the various quantities in fig. 30 for singly charged ions, one sees directly why the levels of negative ions in solution are shifted in the opposite direction to the levels of positive ions —that is to say, one sees how it comes about that J_- is greater than $\mathscr{I}_-$ by the amount W_-, while J is less than $\mathscr{I}$ by the amount W_+.

To deal with ions in higher stages of ionisation, it will be convenient to devise a more systematic notation. We shall say that an ion is "of degree m" when it bears a charge $m\epsilon$. Neutralisation of an ion will then be regarded as reduction to zero degree. The work required to raise the degree of an ion or atom from m to $m+1$ in vacuo is known to spectroscopists as the $(m+1)$th ionisation potential of the element. We may use the notation $_m\mathscr{I}_{m'}$ to denote the work required to raise an ion from degree m to any other degree m' in vacuo, the ordinary first ionisation potential being written $_0\mathscr{I}_1$. The corresponding quantities for ions in solution may be denoted by $_mJ_{m'}$. For example, the depth of the occupied electronic level of Fe^{++} is $_2J_3$, while the depth of the vacant level of Fe^{++} is $_1J_2$.

For positive ions in solution each $_mJ_{m'}$ is less than the corresponding quantity $_m\mathscr{I}_{m'}$ in vacuo, because of the change in the solvation energy which, as we have seen, varies at least as rapidly as m^2. In fact, corresponding to (42) we have

$$_mJ_{m'} = {_m\mathscr{I}_{m'}} - {_mW_{m'}} \qquad \ldots\ldots(43),$$

where $_mW_{m'}$ is the change in the solvation energy on going from degree m to degree m'. The value of $_0J_1$ for singly charged ions, which was deduced in Chapter v and reproduced in expression (42), is a special case of (43). In each case expression (43) may be verified graphically from fig. 30, which shows clearly the relations between the various quantities. For negative ions the generalised form of (41) is likewise

$$_mJ_{m'} = {_m\mathscr{I}_{m'}} + {_mW_{m'}} \qquad \ldots\ldots(44).$$

To sum up, we see that multiply charged ions are not more difficult to deal with than singly charged ions. To remove or add an electron involves a certain change of energy which is quite definite as soon as we specify the initial and final degrees m and m' of the ion. In considering the transfer of an electron between one species of ion and another, or between an ion and a metal, diagrams like figs. 22 and 25 may be used if we insert the electronic level of the ion at the depth corresponding to the appropriate value of $_mJ_{m'}$.

§ 5. TRANSFERENCE OF ELECTRONS

We may begin now to study a solution containing a metal in two stages of ionisation, for example, the mixed ferric and ferrous solution mentioned in § 1. The first point to notice is that no work is required to transfer an electron from a Fe^{++} ion to a Fe^{+++} ion, nor is any energy liberated. The final state has exactly the same energy as the initial state, since, when the electron is transferred the Fe^{++} ion has become Fe^{+++}, while the Fe^{+++} has become Fe^{++}. Though there has been an exchange, we have a pair of ions identical with the initial pair. In any mixed solution containing these ions (or any similar pairs of ions) such transference of electrons is certainly taking place all the time, though it can only be brought to light by the use of isotopes which can be distinguished from each other.

In the case of lead the continual interchange was demonstrated by Hevesy,* using salts of ordinary lead and of a radioactive isotope of lead. In all lead isotopes the 82 electrons surrounding the nucleus have exactly the same configuration, and the nucleus itself bears the same positive charge 82ϵ; the only difference is that of the radioactive nuclei a certain fraction disintegrates in every second. Hevesy prepared from lead, containing a certain amount of a radioactive isotope, some crystals of plumbic acetate which he dissolved in hot glacial acetic acid. He likewise prepared a similar solution of plumbous acetate from ordinary lead. On mixing the solutions and cooling, the plumbic salt crystallised out. After these crystals had been washed and dried, their radioactivity was measured by direct comparison with a specimen of the original plumbic acetate.

If no interchange had taken place, the radioactivity of a given quantity would be the same as before, for the lead crystallising out would be the same as was present in the initial plumbic salt. It was found, however, that, within the experimental error, the radioactivity had become halved. Half of the radioactive lead had remained behind in the solution and had been replaced by ordinary lead. In the solution there had evidently been time for complete interchange to take place.

The corresponding experiment was performed starting with radioactive plumbous acetate and ordinary plumbic acetate. There had again been time for the radioactive atoms to distribute themselves equally, for it was found that just half the radioactivity had been transferred from the plumbous to the plumbic form.

Interchange of this kind is certainly a general feature of such solutions. And we must go on now to apply the same ideas when an electrode is introduced into the solution. Let us take, for example, the half-cell mentioned in § 1, where a piece of platinum was dipping into a mixed ferric-ferrous solution. In the neighbourhood of the platinum surface there will be some ions of each kind, and we must take the point of view that all

* *Berichte*, **53**, 410 (1920).

the time electrons are escaping from the metal to certain Fe^{+++} ions, while other electrons are escaping to the metal from certain Fe^{++} ions. We must still take this point of view when a small current is flowing through the half-cell. A description has already been given at the end of the preceding chapter of the way in which a small current will flow in either direction through the half-cell, when it is coupled with any other half-cell. And this we must now describe by saying that the number of electrons passing per second from the metal to the Fe^{+++} is either greater than the number of electrons passing from the Fe^{++} to the metal, or it is less, according to the direction in which the current is flowing. Electrons are passing in both directions, in and out of the metal, and the value of the current is given by the excess of one over the other.

The most striking feature of this process is the ease with which a doubly or trebly charged ion gives up a third or fourth electron. We know that this process takes place at the enormously high temperatures in the centre of a star; but it is at first a little surprising to find it happening so readily at room temperature.

In Chapter III we described the escape of an electron from a negative ion to a metal, and from a neutral atom to a metal. But the occupied level of every singly charged positive ion *in vacuo* is so low that the escape of an electron from a positive ion to a metal is a process which never needs to be discussed. It would require a surface double layer of many ϵ-volts to bring the occupied level of any positive ion above the critical level of the metal. The occupied level of every doubly charged ion is, of course, much lower still; as was mentioned in Chapter II, if one considers the values of successive ionisation potentials $\mathscr{I}$, $\mathscr{I}_+$ and $\mathscr{I}_{++}$, for any element, one finds a fairly rapid progression, each being markedly larger than the last. For ions in solution, on the other hand, this familiar type of progression is often absent. Although in fig. 30a the vertical distance representing J_+ has been drawn greater than J, this clearly need not be so. We have seen that the solvation energy of a doubly charged ion may be four times as great as for a singly charged ion, or even more. And this may bring the minimum of the upper curve lower than has been drawn in fig. 30 a. Whereas for an atom *in vacuo* the work to remove two electrons is always much greater than twice the work to remove one, in solution it need not be; it may even be less than twice.

§ 6. ELECTRONIC EQUILIBRIUM IN A HALF-CELL

When an insulated piece of platinum is dipping into a ferrous-ferric or other mixed solution, the number of electrons leaving the metal per second must become equal to the number of electrons entering it. At the first moment when the piece of metal is dipped into the solution there is no reason why these numbers should be equal. If the number of electrons leaving the metal is initially greater, the metal immediately begins to acquire a positive charge, and there grows up an electrical double layer, negative outwards, which checks the escape of electrons. Conversely, if the number of electrons entering the metal is initially greater, there grows up an electrical double layer, positive outwards, which checks the entry of electrons, and assists their escape. The number of electrons leaving the metal depends upon the concentration of Fe^{+++} ions ready to receive them, while the number of electrons entering the metal depends on the concentration of the Fe^{++} ions from which they come. The equilibrium value of the electrical double layer depends, as we shall see, on the ratio of these two concentrations. In order to discover what other factors are involved, it will be useful to begin by considering only those mixed solutions in which the ratio of the two concentrations has been chosen equal to unity. Such solutions we shall refer to as standard mixed solutions.

We have seen that in a metal at room temperature the electron levels at the "critical" level are half filled with electrons. A little above the critical level the levels become nearly empty, while a little below they become nearly full. We can see that if at any moment many electrons are escaping from the metal into the solution, the vacant level of the Fe^{+++} ions cannot at any rate be more than a little above the critical level of the metal (compare fig. 25). And if many electrons are entering the metal we can say that the occupied level of the Fe^{++} ions cannot at any rate be more than a little below the critical level of the metal. But we are now familiar with the idea that the depth of the vacant level of Fe^{+++} is identical with the depth of the occupied level of Fe^{++}; they are, in fact, different names for the same quantity $_2J_3$. What we are concerned with is the position of this electronic level of the ions relative to the electronic levels of the metal. We have seen that for equilibrium it must be quite near the critical level of the metal. If there exists an insoluble metal with a work-function whose value is approximately equal to $_2J_3$, then on dipping this metal into the standard solution, scarcely any electrical double layer will be needed to set up equilibrium. If, on the other hand, the value of ϕ for the metal electrode is considerably greater than $_2J_3$, the electronic level of the ion must be lowered, which will require a double layer negative inwards; and if ϕ is less than $_2J_3$, it will require a double layer positive inwards. The argument must run very like that given in Chapter VII for metallic cores, where we considered in turn elements for which $W = Y$, for which $W < Y$, and for which $W > Y$. In fig. 30 belonging to each of the potential valleys there was a set of vibrational levels; so here the Fe^{++} ion possesses a set of vibrational levels belonging to its potential valley of fig. 30a, and so does Fe^{+++}. When Fe^{++} is in its lowest level the work to remove an electron is $_2J_3$. If the electron were not escaping to an electrode, this would be the work required to pass from state 2 to state 1. But as the electron is escaping to the critical level of the metal, the work (in the absence of any double layer at the interface) will be $(_2J_3 - \phi)$. This quantity corresponds to $(Y - W)$ in the other problem.

We may notice that in any half-cell the states 1 and 2 are always defined with respect to the electrode; for even when the electrode is insoluble and acts merely as a channel for the electrons, the value of its work function enters into the definition of the energies of the conjugate states of the half-cell. Further, as we know, any electrical double layer over the surface of the electrode immediately shifts one set of levels with respect to the other set.

Among the other mixed solutions which behave like Fe^{+++}–Fe^{++} may be mentioned Ti^{+++}–Ti^{++}, Cr^{+++}–Cr^{++}, Ce^{++++}–Ce^{+++}, and Co^{+++}–Co^{++}. If we make up half-cells with standard mixed solutions of each of these elements, we can obtain direct information as to the relative values of the ionisation potential of their ions. On coupling together any two standard half-cells with a platinum electrode in each, a difference of potential will be found between the terminals unless the value of $_mJ_{m'}$ for one of the elements happens to be the same as the value of $_mJ_{m'}$ for the other. The terminal of a half-cell will be negative with respect to the terminal of any half-cell whose ions have a greater value of $_mJ_{m'}$.

CHAPTER X

§ 1. EQUILIBRIUM IN ANY HALF-CELL

Having looked at three or four different types of half-cell we may now carry further the scheme of generalisation which was begun in Chapter VIII. According to our definition the substance in state 1 changes into state 2 when electrons are supplied through the electrode. The five possible ways in which the two states may differ from one another are shown in Table III.

TABLE III

	State 1	State 2
1.	A positive ion of degree m which changes to	a positive ion with a smaller charge $(m-1)$ or $(m-2)$.
2.	A positive ion which changes to	neutral substance.
3.	Neutral substance changes to	negative ion.
4.	Negative ion changes to	negative ion with greater charge.
5.	Positive ion changes to	negative ion.

The ferric-ferrous half-cell is clearly an example of the first type, while the iodine half-cell which we described belongs to the third type. Probably half-cells of type 5 do not occur. The well-known hydrogen half-cell, containing hydrogen positive ions and neutral hydrogen, is an example of type 2; and under this heading must also be placed every soluble metal electrode. In this chapter we shall confine attention almost entirely to half-cells containing insoluble electrodes, since soluble electrodes present various peculiar features. We have already noticed that in such a half-cell only one of the two conjugate concentrations is subject to choice. Further, when a soluble electrode is dissolving away or growing by deposition, electrons are not flowing through a fixed double layer, but the position of the double layer is itself continually shifting. On the other hand, when the electrode is insoluble, the position of the double layer is fixed and we can visualise the passage of a definite number of electrons through this double layer without the least ambiguity. When a current is flowing through the half-cell, and the substance is changing from state 1 to state 2 or vice versa, in respect of each particle so changing, either 1, 2 or n electrons, as the case may be, have to pass through the double layer.

From this point of view we must draw a distinction between two classes of half-cells. In the ferric-ferrous type one Fe ion of degree m changes to one ion of degree m'; there is a one-one correspondence between the particles at concentration c_1 and those at concentration c_2. In the iodine half-cell this is not so. Here c_1 measures the concentration of the neutral iodine in solution, which is not atomic but molecular. When a current flows, one particle at concentration c_1 goes to form two particles at concentration c_2. This type of half-cell requires a longer discussion, and in this chapter the expressions (46) and (47) which we shall give will apply only to those half-cells where there is a one-one correspondence. The general principles, however, are the same for all kinds.

A half-cell belonging to any of the types in Table III may be coupled either to another half-cell of the same type, or to a half-cell of a different type. In every complete cell the reaction accompanying the flow of current is one which could be carried out directly by mixing the reagents. Our aim in every case is to use the observed value of the e.m.f. to deduce the characteristic energies of the solvated ions. Since the e.m.f. depends on the concentrations, we must, as already mentioned, understand how the concentration factors may be exactly eliminated.

In state 1 the substance possesses a set of quantised energy levels, and in state 2 it possesses another set of quantised levels. Let the energy of the lowest level of the former be denoted by E_1 and of the latter by E_2. As we have seen, an electrical double layer at the interface has the effect of shifting one of these sets of levels relative to the other set. Consider first the situation when no electrical double layer is present at the interface. To change a particle from the level E_1 to the level E_2 an amount of work $(E_2 - E_1)$ is required. This quantity may be positive or negative; its magnitude may be small or large. The essential condition for reversible equilibrium is that transitions can take place readily in both directions, which is impossible when the base of one set of levels lies much higher than the base of the other set. When the magnitude of $(E_1 - E_2)$ is large, there must grow up a double layer whose sign and magnitude are such as to equalise the situation by diminishing the interval from $(E_1 - E_2)$ to

$$(E_1 - E_2 - n\epsilon V) \qquad \ldots\ldots(45).$$

The exact value which V must take depends on the ratio of the conjugate concentrations c_1 and c_2. It is only in special circumstances that the value of (45) must at equilibrium become actually zero. A zero value is required only when the transfer of a particle from state 1 to state 2 or vice versa is attended by no change of entropy; there is always a change of entropy except when the ratio of the concentrations has been specially chosen. If we know how to choose such a ratio—which we may call an isentropic ratio—we shall be able to eliminate the concentration factor, and $n\epsilon V$ will be just equal to $(E_1 - E_2)$.

At any temperature T we shall then have two Boltzmann distributions, the base of one being E_1, the base of the other being E_2. The equilibrium between two Boltzmann distributions has already been considered in Chapter VII; it was mentioned there that the analysis would be applicable to other types of electrode.

Although in different types of half-cell the substance in either state may be positive, neutral, or negative, our definition enables us to make statements which will be true of every type. Increasing the concentration of the substance in state 1 invariably causes the electrode to become more positive with respect to the solution; that is, the electrical double layer at the interface becomes more negative outwards, or less positive outwards. Conversely, if we alter the concentration of the substance in state 2, whether this substance consists of positive ions, neutral particles, or negative ions—in every case if we increase c_2, leaving c_1 unaltered, this causes the potential of the metal electrode to become more negative with respect to the solution, and consequently more negative with respect to the electrode of any half-cell with which this half-cell is coupled.

For equilibrium between the two Boltzmann distributions we shall have, corresponding to (30) and (35),

$$c_1 \exp{(E_1 - n\epsilon V - E)}/kT = \beta c_2 \exp{(E_2 - E)}/kT \quad \ldots\ldots(46),$$

$$V = \frac{E_1 - E_2}{n\epsilon} + \frac{kT}{n\epsilon} \log{\frac{f_1 c_1}{f_2 c_2}} \qquad \ldots\ldots(47).$$

A rigorous treatment of the equilibrium leads to the same expression.

§ 2. PRACTICAL ELECTRODE POTENTIALS

The coupling together of two half-cells has already been considered qualitatively. We wish now to use experimental values of e.m.f.'s to obtain information about the characteristic energies of ions. For this purpose we must consider briefly the conventions used in tabulating observed values of e.m.f.'s. As the e.m.f. of a cell depends on the temperature and on the concentrations, it is important to record accurate values of e.m.f. for cells in an agreed standard state. A temperature of 25° C. is usually adopted, and one mol per litre is taken as unit concentration for the ions. The value usually tabulated is the e.m.f. which the cell would have with the ions, not at unit concentration, but at unit activity, a condition which was defined in Chapter VII.

Since the two halves of any cell operate independently, in any complete cell each half-cell makes its own contribution to the total e.m.f. Rather than tabulate the e.m.f.'s of complete cells, it would obviously be preferable, if it were possible, to have a list recording the contribution made by each half-cell which has been investigated. Then for any complete cell formed from any two of the half-cells, the e.m.f. would be simply the sum of the contributions. For practical purposes it is only necessary to allot to each half-cell an arbitrary number, such that, when we couple together any two half-cells, the value of the e.m.f. in volts will be given by the difference between the numbers which have been allotted to the two half-cells. To obtain such a list of numbers, it is only necessary to choose some particular half-cell as a universal reference electrode. Suppose that A, B and C in fig. 28 are three reversible half-cells containing different substances dissolved in the same solvent. The e.m.f. of the cell AB is independent of the presence of C, and is equal to the sum of the e.m.f.'s of the cells AC and CB. (Having regard to sign, the sum of the e.m.f.'s of any two cells AC and CB is equal to the difference of the e.m.f.'s of AC and BC.) The e.m.f. of the cell AB is thus divided arbitrarily into two unequal parts, which may be regarded as the contributions of the half-cell A and the half-cell B, respectively. Suppose now that the half-cell B is replaced by a different half-cell D. If the e.m.f. of the cell DC is regarded as the contribution of the half-cell D, that ascribed to the half-cell A is the same as before, namely the e.m.f. of the cell AC. For systematic correlation of all half-cells containing aqueous solutions there is an international agreement as to the particular half-cell which is to be used for the reference electrode C. This is a standard hydrogen half-cell in which the neutral hydrogen in solution is in equilibrium with gaseous hydrogen at a pressure of one atmosphere, and the hydrogen ions are at unit activity.

In every simple isometallic cell the e.m.f. is just the algebraic sum of the strengths of the electrical double layers at the solid-liquid interface in each half-cell. The strength of the double layer has a value which is quite independent of that in the other half-cell to which it is coupled. In contrast to the arbitrary numbers which we have described above, it is clear that in any isometallic cell the true contribution of each half-cell is quite definite and not in any way arbitrary. In a simple bimetallic cell the e.m.f. is the algebraic sum of the strengths of three electrical double layers. The discussion of bimetallic cells will be postponed to Chapter xv; in this chapter we shall consider only cells in which both electrodes are of the same metal. For each half-cell we have an expression (47), and the value of the e.m.f. is obtained by subtracting one from the other.

If the electrode of one half-cell A is positive with respect to the electrode of the half-cell B, this does not, of course, imply that the electrode of A is necessarily positive with respect to the solution within the cell; there are three possibilities for the pair of electrical double layers: (1) both electrodes are positive with respect to the solution, A being more positive than B, (2) both electrodes are negative with respect to the solution, B being more negative than A, and (3) A is positive with respect to the solution and B is negative with respect to the solution.

§ 3. CONCENTRATION CELLS

A change in the electrical double layer in one half-cell implies, of course, an equal change in the e.m.f. of the cell. In any complete cell we have in general four concentrations, namely the two in each half-cell. It has long been known that if we alter one of these four concentrations, leaving the other three un-altered—if, say, in one half-cell we alter c_1 to the value c_1'— then the change in the e.m.f. of the cell, expressed in volts, will at room temperature be given very nearly by

$$\frac{0 \cdot 025}{n} \log_e \frac{c'}{c} = \frac{0 \cdot 059}{n} \log_{10} \frac{c'}{c} \qquad \ldots\ldots(48),$$

where n has the meaning given above. This result is to be expected from (47), since the numerical value of kT at room temperature is $0 \cdot 025$ ϵ-volt.

In this connection we may in passing mention what are known as concentration cells. Suppose that we couple together two half-cells which are identical except in respect of one of the concentrations, say that of state 1, which has the value c_1 in one half-cell, and c_1' in the other, the value of c_2 being the same in both half-cells. The values of E_1 and E_2 will be the same in both, and it is clear from (47) that in dilute solution the double layer at the interface in one half-cell will differ from that in the other by just the amount (48). Apart from the liquid junction, the complete cell will possess an e.m.f. of this value. This fact has long been understood from thermodynamic reasoning. When the external circuit of the cell is closed, and a charge is allowed to flow, in one half-cell a certain amount of substance is removed from state 1 at concentration c_1, and in the other half-cell an equal amount of substance enters state 1 at a concentration c_1'. In other words, the substance is brought from concentration c_1 to c_1', for which, according to (23) an amount of work $kT \log f_1 c_1 / f_1' c_1'$ per molecule is required. It is unnecessary to mention the loss and gain of substance in state 2, because the concentration c_2 is the same in both half-cells.

§ 4. IONISATION POTENTIALS AND E.M.F.

We are interested in cells of the opposite type, where the concentration term is zero, and the e.m.f. is determined only by the energies E in each half-cell. We may at last begin to draw the quantitative conclusions, for the sake of which the discussion of cells was introduced in the first place. Table IV gives the

TABLE IV

STANDARD OXIDATION-REDUCTION POTENTIALS IN AQUEOUS
SOLUTION REFERRED TO THE HYDROGEN ELECTRODE

		Volts
Cr^{+++}	Cr^{++}	-0.4
Ti^{+++}	Ti^{++}	$+0.37$
Fe^{+++}	Fe^{++}	$+0.75$
Ce^{++++}	Ce^{+++}	$+1.55$
Co^{+++}	Co^{++}	$+1.82$

results for half-cells of the ferric-ferrous type, taken from the International Critical Tables. Fortunately, the values refer to half-cells where the ions of degree m and those of degree m' were at equal activity, which is just the condition which eliminates the term $kT \log a_1 / a_2$.

At the end of the preceding chapter we saw how equilibrium is set up between the ions and an insulated electrode. An ion changes from state 1 to state 2 when one electron escapes from the metal to the ion. In this half-cell we clearly have

$$(E_1 - E_2 - n \epsilon V) = (_m J_{m'} - \phi - \epsilon V) \qquad \ldots \ldots (49).$$

If we couple together two half-cells of this type, one containing ions of a metal A and the other ions of a metal B, the ratio of the concentrations being in both cases isentropic, we have, omitting the subscripts m and m',

$$\epsilon V_A = J_A - \phi \quad \text{and} \quad \epsilon V_B = J_B - \phi \qquad \ldots\ldots(50).$$

There is no doubt as to the direction in which the spontaneous current will flow. The electrode of the half-cell whose ion has the lower electronic level will be positive with respect to the other. That is to say, the spontaneous current which flows consists of electrons coming from the occupied level of one species of ion and passing to the lower vacant level of the ions of the other metal, as would happen in direct mixing.

The potential difference between the electrodes, that is, the value of the e.m.f. $\mathscr{E}$, is given by

$$\epsilon \mathscr{E} = \epsilon \,(V_A - V_B) = J_A - J_B \qquad \ldots\ldots(51).$$

The value of the e.m.f. in volts is the same as the difference between the ionisation potentials expressed in ϵ-volts. We conclude then that the difference between any pair of numbers in Table IV gives the difference between the electronic levels of the ions. Accordingly the ion Ce^{++++} will capture an electron from Fe^{++}, the ion Fe^{+++} will capture an electron from the ion Ti^{++} or from the ion Cr^{++}, either by direct encounter or by the intermediacy of electrodes. The occupied electronic level of Cr^{++} is, we see, about $2\cdot2$ ϵ-volts higher than the occupied level of Co^{++}.

CHAPTER XI

§ 1. THE DEGREE OF DISSOCIATION INTO IONS

In Chapter IX mention was made of the early ideas regarding conducting solutions. It was at first suggested that the application of an external field had the effect of breaking some molecules into ions, which recombined as soon as the field was removed. Later the idea that some of the molecules were permanently dissociated into ions received support from evidence which appeared to show that the osmotic pressure of conducting solutions was higher than that of non-conducting solutions.

When in this chapter, employing the usual terminology, we speak of osmotic coefficients, and cite experimental results, these values have for the most part been obtained, not by direct measurement of the osmotic pressure, but by one or the other of the well-known indirect methods. For example, when a solution is frozen, pure solvent crystallises out. In order that any crystal of solvent may grow, the particles of solute must obviously be driven back. In growing, each crystal of pure solvent has to make room for itself against the osmotic pressure of the solute, the value of which is obtained by observing the freezing point of the solution. Results derived in this way are in good agreement with those obtained from measurements of the vapour pressure of the solution.

For a 1/10th molar solution of KCl in water the osmotic pressure was found to be some 80 per cent. greater than for a substance like sugar at the same concentration. This was taken to mean that the molecules of KCl were about 80 per cent. dissociated into ions in this solution. Similarly for a 1/10th molar solution of $BaCl_2$ the osmotic pressure was as much as 2·5 times the normal value, indicating that some molecules had been dissociated into three ions (see Table V). For the same substance dissolved in organic solvents the osmotic pressure was usually much nearer the normal value. This was taken to mean that in non-aqueous solvents the substances were dissociated into ions to a much smaller extent.

It was mentioned in Chapter II that the law of mass action in the simple form $\alpha^2/(1-\alpha) \propto v$ applies only to a substance behaving as a perfect gas. Nevertheless an imperfect gas or solute will follow a similar course, tending towards complete dissociation at infinite dilution. In the solutions cited below the numbers should, therefore, be found to tend to 2 for salts like KCl and $MgSO_4$, to 3 for salts like $BaCl_2$, and to 4 for trivalent salts. The examples of aqueous solutions given in Table V are consistent with this rule.

TABLE V

$\gamma =$ CONCENTRATION IN MOLS PER 1000 GR. OF WATER

$i =$ RATIO OF OBSERVED OSMOTIC PRESSURE TO THE
VALUE FOR UNDISSOCIATED MOLECULES

KCl		MgSO$_4$	
γ	i	γ	i
0·0010	1·97	0·0049	1·60
0·0100	1·94	0·0160	1·48

BaCl$_2$		La(NO$_3$)$_3$	
γ	i	γ	i
0·00087	2·86	0·00132	3·75
0·0114	2·72	0·00806	3·40

As already mentioned, values of i like those given in Table V, deduced from different properties of the same solution, were found to be in agreement with one another. Since, however, these alternative experimental methods of determining the supposed equilibrium between neutral molecules and ions all depended on the osmotic pressure, it was very desirable to have an independent method, having no connection with osmotic pressure. Measurements of the electrical conductivity of the solutions appeared to fulfil this requirement. When an electric field is applied to a solution, the Brownian movement of each ion is no longer random, but possesses a certain drift in one direction or the other according to the charge borne by the ion.

For any species of ion the value of the drift velocity in unit field depends on the solvent in which the ion is situated, and is known as the mobility of the ion in that solvent. With rise of temperature the viscosity of the solvent decreases rapidly, and the mobility of all ions consequently increases; in this chapter we shall be concerned only with the conductivity at room temperature.

The value of the mobility varies little from one species of ion to another, and so the conductivity of a solution is at least a rough measure of the number of ions present. Many soluble organic substances give feebly conducting solutions, and for these solutions the value of the osmotic pressure supports the idea that at moderate concentrations the solute consists almost entirely of undissociated molecules. On the other hand, inorganic substances soluble in water, with few exceptions, give strongly conducting solutions; in each case the osmotic pressure has a high value, like those of Table V.

In a sufficiently dilute solution the viscous forces limiting the mobility of any ion will be almost identical with those in a pure solvent. It was supposed, therefore, that in very dilute solutions the mobility could be taken as independent of the concentration; in which case the values of the conductivity at various concentrations would be a direct measure of the number of ions present. Now if the ideas of p. 120 are correct, the number of ions will not be proportional to the concentration of the solute, since at higher concentrations more pairs of ions are united to form neutral molecules. If the conductivity is plotted against the concentration, the relation will not be linear; the conductivity will increase less rapidly, due to the progressive increase in the number of neutral molecules which play no part in carrying the current. In other words, the conductivity per gram of substance dissolved will not remain constant, but will fall off steadily with increasing concentration. For all electrolytes the conductivity is, in fact, found to behave in this way. Further, in non-aqueous solutions, judging from the osmotic results, one would expect the presence of neutral molecules to be more marked; and it is found that the equivalent conductivity of non-aqueous solutions falls off even more rapidly than that of aqueous solutions. This was taken to be additional evidence that in non-aqueous solvents molecules are dissociated into ions to a smaller extent than in water.

§ 2. COMPLETE DISSOCIATION

It has already been mentioned that about 1920 the idea became prevalent that crystals of many of the simple salts, such as NaCl, were to be described as consisting, not of neutral NaCl molecules, but of rows of alternate positive and negative ions with their electronic shells in contact. This idea drew attention afresh to a view of electrolytic solutions which had already been mooted more than once. If the positive and negative ions present in the crystal lattice went into solution separately, and all remained as separate positive and negative ions, there would be no neutral solute molecules present at all. We have seen how the experimental results of both the conductivity and osmotic methods appeared to indicate the presence of a proportion of neutral molecules in all solutions, even in dilute solutions of the substances mentioned. If, then, it is true that in many solutions no neutral molecules are present, this agreement must have been fortuitous, and a separate explanation must be found for the experimental results in both classes of phenomena.

As soon as we tentatively adopt the idea of complete dissociation of ions, the quantities on which we fix our attention are changed. In § 1 it was mentioned how in early days the osmotic pressure of electrolytes was found to be greater than that of substances like sugar. But now we no longer wish to explain why the actual osmotic pressure P is *greater* than the osmotic pressure of an ideal solution containing the same number of molecules. On the contrary, we wish to explain why the actual osmotic pressure P is *less* than the osmotic pressure P_0 of an ideal solution containing as many particles as there will be ions in the electrolytic solution, if the solute is completely dissociated.

Our preliminary discussion of this problem was summed up in (20) and (25). Let the ratio between P and P_0 be denoted by g,

$$P = gP_0 \qquad \qquad \ldots\ldots(52).$$

Here g will be a number less than unity, depending on the concentration, and known as the osmotic coefficient of the solution.

§ 3. INTERIONIC FORCES

To evaluate the configuration energy of the solution, we have to consider the interionic forces. Though a positive and a negative ion attract one another, this will change over into the usual intense repulsion when the ions are brought close together. For all species of ions between which the attraction is purely electrostatic, i.e. where no exchange forces contribute towards the attraction, the minimum of the potential energy will be much shallower than for the same ions in a vacuum. Since in the solvent all electrostatic forces are diminished, the depth of the potential valley, instead of being, say, 5 ϵ-volts for a pair of singly charged ions, will be only a small fraction of an ϵ-volt. The bottom of the potential valley will be broad and shallow, as in curve a of fig. 31.

Considering next two of the positive ions, we shall have a curve that is rising all the way—at first slowly, due to the Coulombic repulsion, and then at a certain radius more steeply when the solvated ions are coming into "contact". If the negative ions bear the same charge as the positives, the electrostatic repulsion at long distances will be identical; for large values of r curves b and c coincide; but if the radii of the ions are different, as is generally the case, the steep part of the curve will begin at a larger or smaller value of r.

In this chapter we shall fix our attention almost entirely on those electrolytes where the positive and negative ions bear equal charges and are thus present in equal numbers, such as $MgSO_4$ and $NaCl$. For a pair of doubly charged ions situated in the same solvent, the electrostatic forces are, of course, four times as great as for singly charged ions. We shall, therefore, have a curve falling four times as steeply as curve a, and a curve rising four times as steeply as curves b and c; these are indicated by the dotted curves in fig. 31. For large values of r curve a below the axis is the mirror image of curve b above the axis; and the same is true for the pair of dotted curves.

In the left-hand half of fig. 31 the shapes of the curves are characteristic of the particular species of ions under consideration, depending upon the radii of their electronic configurations, etc. But to the right of some line, like the vertical dotted line in fig. 31, the curves a and b represent purely Coulomb forces and will be the same for any pair of singly charged ions (and curves d and e for any pair of doubly charged ions). Now at very low concentrations of the solute the ions spend most of their time at long distances from one another, and the left-hand side of fig. 31 becomes relatively unimportant. In very dilute

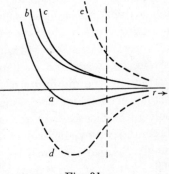

Fig. 31

solutions, then, the problem is much simpler, and any results that we obtain will apply to all species of ions. It is only at higher concentrations that each solute will begin to show individual behaviour.

As far as the kinetic energy of an ion is concerned, this is in equilibrium with the kinetic energy of the solvent molecules by which the ion is being jostled. Its potential energy in the field of the other positive and negative ions will be determined by the appropriate curves of fig. 31. And we can now begin to attack the main problem, by making use of the fact that the number of ions possessing a certain amount of potential energy will be given by the Boltzmann law.

§4. DEBYE-HÜCKEL THEORY

Suppose that we fix our attention on a small volume dv, at a fixed point in the interior of a dilute solution, and observe the ions which enter this volume. We shall find sometimes a positive ion, and sometimes a negative ion, entering and spending either a shorter or longer interval in the volume. But we know that if our observations extend over a period of time long compared with the Brownian movement, the average charge density will be zero. Suppose, on the other hand, that we observe a small volume dv, not at a fixed point in the solution, but at a small distance r from one particular ion, on which we choose to fix our attention; we shall call this ion the "central" ion; as this ion moves about, the volume dv moves with it at a fixed distance r. We wish to show that under these circumstances the average charge density ρ in the volume dv, taken over a sufficiently long period of time, is not zero, but is negative when the central ion is positive, and positive when the central is negative. At large distances the central ion, of course, exerts a negligible influence; hence with increasing r the charge density ρ thins out, and tends to zero.

If V_+ is the potential energy of a positive ion in the volume element dv, the average number of positive ions in this volume element will be, by Boltzmann's law

$$n_+dv = ne^{-V_+/kT}.dv \qquad \ldots\ldots(53).$$

Similarly, if V_- is the potential energy of a negative ion in the same volume element, the average number of negative ions there will be

$$n_-dv = ne^{-V_-/kT}.dv \qquad \ldots\ldots(54).$$

If the temperature is raised, the distribution approaches a uniform random distribution; both n_+ and n_- tend towards n, the number of ion pairs per unit volume.

Let the ions bear charges $\pm q$; then the average charge density is given by

$$\rho = (n_+q - n_-q) \qquad \ldots\ldots(55).$$

The sign of ρ is positive or negative according as the value of

(53) is greater or less than (54). The values of V_+ and V_- depend on whether a positive or negative central ion is under consideration. Let us first take a positive ion as the central ion. We shall use curves a, b and c of fig. 31, if we are dealing with singly charged ions. The potential energy of a positive ion V_+ consists of two parts, the main part due to the repulsion of the central ion, and a smaller part due to the other ions. The former will be given by the ordinate at the appropriate point on curve b or c of fig. 31, corresponding to the distance r under consideration. The potential energy due to the other ions is at present unknown. Similarly V_- consists of two parts, first that due to the central ion, given by the appropriate point on curve a, and secondly that due to the other ions.

For very dilute solutions, as mentioned above, we can simplify the problem by neglecting the left-hand half of fig. 31, taking only the electrostatic portions of the curves, where curve a below the axis is the mirror image of curve b above.

If in the volume dv under consideration the electrostatic potential is ψ, the potential energy of a positive charge q in this volume will be $V_+ = q\psi$, while the potential energy of a negative ion will be $V_- = -q\psi$. We can substitute these values in (53) and (54).

The electrical potential at a distance r from a single charge q is q/Kr. The average potential ψ will differ from this value to some extent, due to the negative charge density round the ion, which we are trying to evaluate. It is easy to see in which direction the value will differ, and where the difference will be greatest. Let the central ion under consideration be a positive ion, bearing a charge q, with a slight excess of negative neighbours. Suppose that we have a free electron, which we let move through this assembly, past the central ion. We wish to know the potential energy of this electron at every point of its path. We may suppose that the electron moves sufficiently fast for the ions to have no time to alter their positions on its account. Let the dotted line EFD of fig. 32 be a plot of $-\epsilon q/Kr$, the potential energy which the electronic charge ϵ would have in the field of the charge q if the neighbours were absent: and consider how the required curve will differ from this. We can say at once (1) that for large values of r the required curve must still become asymptotic to the axis; and (2) that when the electron is extremely near the central ion it is in a field which has the same intensity as if the neighbours were absent.

For the central solvated ion has a certain radius, and no neighbour on collision with it approaches nearer than a certain distance a. For values of r less than a the required curve must have the same slope as if the neighbours were absent; i.e. in this region the curve is the same as EF, only shifted vertically upward or downward. Clearly the shift must be an

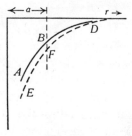

Fig. 32

upward one. For as our electron approaches the central positive ion the slightly negative atmosphere round it exerts a screening effect; the potential energy curve will, therefore, fall less steeply than DF. We require some curve like DBA, whose shape will depend on the concentration of the solution. We shall have to obtain an expression for the curve DB; but our only object in doing so will be to evaluate the vertical distance of AB above EF. For if we consider what this vertical shift represents, we shall see that it gives us the quantity which we require. The curve EF was a plot of $-\epsilon q/Kr$, the potential energy of our electron in the field of the central charge q alone. The curve AB gives the total potential energy $-\epsilon\psi$ in the field of the central charge and its neighbours. If the vertical shift of AB above EF is called $\epsilon\chi$,

$$\epsilon\psi = \epsilon(q/Kr - \chi) \qquad \ldots\ldots(56).$$

The quantity χ is the constant electrical potential within this region due to the neighbours outside. Since the central ion itself is not subject to its own field but only that of its neighbours, its potential energy is just $-q\chi$. This is the quantity we need for the configuration energy of the solution—the work required to remove an ion from its neighbours.

To obtain an expression for ψ, Debye and Hückel made use of the fact that it must be connected with the average density ρ by Poisson's equation

$$\nabla^2 \psi = -\frac{4\pi\rho}{K} \qquad \ldots\ldots(57),$$

which from (56) and (54) gives

$$\nabla^2 \psi = +\frac{4\pi}{K}\, n\, (e^{q\psi/kT} - e^{-q\psi/kT}) \qquad \ldots\ldots(58).$$

For larger values of r than those included in fig. 31 both the curves lie nearer the axis, so that the value of ψ is everywhere less than 1/100 of an ϵ-volt. In obtaining (58) for dilute solution, we have already made the approximation of neglecting the left-hand half of fig. 31. If we go on now to consider still more dilute solutions, we may suppose that the ions spend so little of their time near to each other that we may make the further approximation of taking into account only those large values of r where $q\psi$ is small compared with the thermal energy kT (1/40 of an ϵ-volt at room temperature). Since, when x is any number small compared with unity, e^x is approximately equal to $(1+x)$, the bracket in (58) will reduce to $2q\psi/kT$, and (58) may be written

$$\nabla^2 \psi = \psi/l^2 \qquad \ldots\ldots(59),$$

where l is a length given by

$$l = \sqrt{\frac{KkT}{8\pi nq^2}} = \sqrt{\frac{Kb^3}{q^2} \cdot \frac{kT}{8\pi}} \qquad \ldots\ldots(60),$$

b being the length defined by (21). The solution of (59), which tends to zero for large values of r, is

$$\psi = \frac{Ae^{-r/l}}{r} \qquad \ldots\ldots(61).$$

When the value of the arbitrary constant A has been correctly chosen, we can obtain an expression for the curve BD in fig. 32. Further, the intensity of the electrostatic field in this region is found by differentiating (61) with respect to r. This gives

$$\frac{d\psi}{dr} = -\frac{Ae^{-r/l}}{r^2}\,(1+r/l) \qquad \ldots\ldots(62).$$

In particular, the intensity of the field at $r=a$ can be obtained by substituting in this expression. But we already know the intensity here. In the region AB of fig. 32 the field is simply q/r^2 due to the central charge, and is consequently q/a^2 at $r=a$. Equating these two expressions we find

$$A = \frac{q}{K} \frac{e^{a/l}}{(1+a/l)} \qquad \ldots\ldots(63).$$

We have now all the material needed for finding the configuration energy of a solution. For, writing $r=a$ in (56) and in (61), and substituting for A, we find

$$q\chi = q^2 \left(\frac{1}{Ka} - \frac{1}{Ka\,(1+a/l)} \right)$$

$$= \frac{q^2}{Kl\,(1+a/l)} \qquad \ldots\ldots(64).$$

In the very dilute solutions with which we are dealing the radius a is small compared with the length l; at the lowest concentrations a/l in the bracket is small compared with unity, and may be omitted. The work required to remove an ion from its neighbours when there are n ion pairs per cm.^{3} is then simply

$$q\chi = \frac{q^2}{Kl} \qquad \ldots\ldots(65)$$

$$= \frac{q^3}{K^{\frac{3}{2}}b^{\frac{3}{2}}} \sqrt{\frac{8\pi}{kT}} \qquad \ldots\ldots(66).$$

For a negative charge it has the same value as for an equal positive charge. The following expressions are useful for ions bearing charges $\pm m\epsilon$:

$$\chi = \frac{m\epsilon}{Kl} = B\,(m\epsilon)^2 = Cv^{-\frac{1}{2}} \qquad \ldots\ldots(67),$$

where $\qquad B = \sqrt{\frac{8\pi n}{K^3 kT}} \quad$ and $\quad C = (m\epsilon)^2 \sqrt{\frac{4\pi N}{K^3 kT}}.$

To obtain the electrostatic potential energy of a solution containing altogether N ions (that is $2nv$ ions in v cm.^{3}), we make

use of the expression (6) given at the end of Chapter I. The value
is clearly
$$\tfrac{1}{2}\,(2nvq\chi) = \tfrac{1}{2}BN\,(m\epsilon)^3 \qquad \ldots\ldots(68).$$

In § 1 of Chapter VII the questions were raised (a) as to whether
ions take up the same average configuration in different solvents,
(b) whether the average configuration at any concentration is
the same at all other concentrations, and (c) whether the average
configuration of the ions will be the same as if we substitute
doubly charged ions for singly charged ions. It was shown that
if conditions (a), (b) and (c) are fulfilled, the quasi-lattice energy
will vary as q^2, as $1/K$ and as $1/b$. It is clear now that the answers
to all three questions are in the negative. The essential feature
of the average configuration in any ionic solution is a discrimination between like and unlike neighbours. The sharpness of this
discrimination is determined by the average strength of the
electrostatic attraction and repulsion between the ions.

If we compare the same ions in two different solvents, there
will be a more intense discrimination in the solvent whose
dielectric constant is lower; the configuration which the ions
will take up will itself be such as to give a greater quasi-lattice
energy, quite apart from the increase (proportional to $1/K$)
which there would have been if the configuration had remained
the same. The value will thus vary more rapidly than $1/K$; in
fact, we see from (66) that it varies inversely as $K^{\frac{3}{2}}$.

Let us take next the question of the ionic charges. If for
singly charged ions we substitute doubly charged ions at the
same concentration, the more intense forces will again produce
a sharper discrimination. This will give a greater quasi-lattice
energy, quite apart from the four-fold increase which there
would have been if the configuration had remained the same.
We see from (66) that the value varies, not as q^2, but as q^3.

Finally there is the question of a simple change of concentration. If we diminish the volume in which the ions are contained,
and so diminish the average distances between them, the stronger
forces produce a greater discrimination between like and unlike
neighbours. The relative position of the ions is not a replica

of what it would be at a lower concentration. The energy, therefore, varies more rapidly than $1/b$; we see from (66) that it
varies inversely as $b^{\frac{3}{2}}$.

These features of the problem are clearly brought out if we
write (65) in the form

$$q\chi = \frac{q^2}{Kb}\sqrt{\frac{q^2}{Kb} \div \frac{kT}{8\pi}} \qquad \ldots\ldots(69).$$

The quantity under the square-root may be termed the "configuration factor", multiplying the purely electrostatic term.
The fact that the state of the solution is governed by a balance
between the electrostatic forces and the thermal agitation is
represented by this quantity under the square-root sign, which
is simply a ratio between the electrostatic energy and the thermal
energy.

§ 5. THE FREE ENERGY

In Chapter VII we imagined a solution contained in a cylinder
provided with a semi-permeable membrane, and considered the
heat which will flow into the solution from the surroundings
when an isothermal expansion takes place. We must now enquire
whether the presence of electrostatic forces will cause any alteration in the amount of heat which flows. If it does, this will
mean a further alteration in the amount of work, and hence a
further alteration in the osmotic pressure. The quantity (68) is
the electrostatic potential energy of the solute, but nothing has
been said as to whether in an isothermal expansion some of the
requisite energy enters the solution in the form of heat.

The problem may be stated in another way. We have said
that, when we compress an ionic solution, we have to do less
than the normal amount of work, because the solute falls to a
state of lower electrostatic energy. But we must now ask the
question—When it falls to the state of lower potential energy,
is any of this energy lost to the surroundings in the form of
heat? If some is lost, the diminution in the osmotic work will
not be as great as if none were lost.

An infinitely slow isothermal expansion is not the only way in which we may imagine the interionic forces reduced reversibly to zero. Keeping the volume of the solution unchanged, we may destroy the electrostatic forces by allowing the positive and negative charges to neutralise one another. We shall do this, not by transferring an electron from each negative ion to a positive, but by the entirely imaginary process of conveying indefinitely small elements of electricity δq from one species to the other until, finally, we have a solution of neutral particles.

In Chapter I we mentioned the method of calculating the energy of a charged body, either in a vacuum or in a solvent, by imagining the charge brought up as indefinitely small elements δq. The answer to our problem is most easily found by carrying out a similar process, not for a single charge, but for an assembly of charges. Let us start then with a solution containing singly charged ions, A^+ and $X^- - n$ of each per cubic centimetre. We will convert this into a solution containing only neutral particles A and X at the same concentration. As we have said, we shall do this reversibly by systematically conveying elements of charge δq from one species to the other, until finally all the particles become neutral simultaneously.

The expressions (59) to (65) are true whether q is an integral multiple of the electronic charge ϵ or not. We are going to suppose that on each positive ion the value of q falls continuously from ϵ to 0, and on each negative ion from $-\epsilon$ to 0. Meanwhile the electric potential due to the neighbouring charges will everywhere fall to zero. In carrying out the neutralisation we have, of course, to supply the solvation energy of each ion, which was dealt with in Chapter I; in this chapter we are concerned only with the interionic forces. When we consider the work required to transfer an element of positive electricity δq from an A^+ to an X^-, we are concerned only with the forces between δq and the neighbours of A^+ and X^-. The ion A^+ is surrounded by an excess of negative neighbours, and an amount of work $\chi \delta q$ has to be done to remove the positive charge δq from their attraction. Further, the ion X^- is surrounded by an excess of positive neighbours; to bring up the positive charge δq against their repulsion requires an amount of work $\chi \delta q$. To put this more simply, we are conveying the charge δq from a place where the electrical potential is $-\chi$ to a place where it is $+\chi$. The work required is $2\chi\delta q$, and the work to do this for n ion pairs amounts to $2n\chi\delta q$.

Further elements of charge are to be transferred until all the ions have become neutral particles. If during this process the initial configuration of the ions were preserved throughout, we should find for the total work $\frac{1}{2}BN(m\epsilon)^3$ as in (68) above. But as the charges on the ions grow smaller, the temperature of the solution T remaining constant, the configuration becomes progressively more random, until finally it is completely random. We shall find that during this process heat flows into the solution and does some of the work against the electrostatic forces. To obtain the work done in neutralising N ions, we have to integrate $2n v \chi dq$ from ϵ to 0 for singly charged ions, and from $m\epsilon$ to 0 for multiply charged ions

$$\int_{m\epsilon}^{0} 2nvBq^2 dq = \tfrac{1}{3}NB(m\epsilon)^3 \qquad \ldots\ldots(70).$$

The difference between this quantity and (68) represents the amount of heat which flows into the solution.

To find the osmotic coefficient of the solution, we have to differentiate (70) with respect to the volume v. From (67), (25), and (52) we find

$$(1-g)P_0 = P_0 - P = \frac{dF_e}{dv} = \frac{d}{dv}\left(\frac{1}{3}NB(m\epsilon)^3\right) \quad \ldots(71)$$

$$= \tfrac{1}{3}Nm\epsilon \frac{d}{dv} Cv^{-\frac{1}{2}}$$

$$= G\left(\frac{m^2 n}{K}\right)^{\frac{3}{2}} \qquad \ldots\ldots(72),$$

where $$G = \frac{\epsilon^3}{3}\sqrt{\frac{8\pi}{kT}} \qquad \ldots\ldots(73).$$

§ 6. COMPARISON WITH EXPERIMENT

We are at last in a position to answer the main question raised in this chapter—whether it is possible to account for the behaviour of dilute solutions without assuming the presence of neutral molecules. To take a numerical example, we may evaluate (72) for 1/500th molar solutions of various univalent electrolytes in different solvents, and see whether it is sufficiently large, compared with P_0, to account for the values of i given in Table V. It is convenient to remember that a pressure of one atmosphere is a million dynes per square centimetre—that is for a gas at room temperature, i.e. containing $2 \cdot 7 \times 10^{19}$ molecules per cm.^{3}. A 1/100th molar solution contains 6×10^{18} molecules per cm.^{3} and exerts an osmotic pressure $0 \cdot 22$ of an atmosphere. For a 1/500th molar solution of an electrolyte completely dissociated into pairs of ions the value of the ideal osmotic pressure P_0 is thus about 88,000 dynes per cm.^{2}.

At room temperature the value of (71) is found to be

$$\partial F/\partial v = 8 \cdot 7 \times 10^{-22} \left(\frac{m^2 n}{K} \right)^{\frac{3}{2}} \text{ dynes/cm.}^2 \quad \ldots \ldots (74).$$

As examples we may take:

(1) A solution of KCl in water at 1/500 molar, for which $m = 1$, $K = 80$ and $n = 1 \cdot 2 \times 10^{18}$. The value of (74) is found to be 1600 dynes per cm.^{2}. We see that even at this low concentration the electrostatic forces between the ions are sufficient to make an appreciable reduction in the osmotic pressure, so that the electrolyte would appear to contain about 3 per cent. of undissociated molecules; the order of magnitude agrees with Table V.

(2) The effect is far more marked if we pass on to $MgSO_4$ in aqueous solution. At the same concentration the value of (74) will be m^3 times greater, that is, eight times greater. Even at 1/500th molar the solution will, according to (74), appear to contain more than 20 per cent. of neutral molecules, even if dissociation is in reality complete. This is again in agreement with the values given for $MgSO_4$ in Table V.

(3) Let us return now to KCl, but dissolved in a solvent of low dielectric constant. In cyclohexanol, for which $K = 15$, the effect will be more than twelve times as great as in water at the same concentration. It is not surprising then that the presence of large quantities of neutral molecules in dilute non-aqueous solutions of electrolytes has been, and still is, taken as an established fact.

(4) For doubly charged ions in a solvent of low dielectric constant the factors just considered in (2) and (3) would both be present, and would give rise to an effect anything up to 100 times as great as for KCl at the same concentration in water. We must expect their behaviour to be quite different except perhaps at concentrations too low for experimental work.

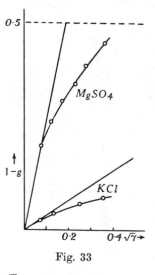

Fig. 33

In the above paragraph we have been evaluating the ratio of $(P_0 - P)$ to P, at a specimen concentration. To exhibit a general comparison it is convenient to plot theoretical and experimental values of this ratio in a diagram. From (74) we see that the theoretical value of $(P_0 - P)$ is proportional to $n^{\frac{3}{2}}$, while from (22) P_0 is proportional to n. In very dilute solutions, therefore, the ratio $(P_0 - P)/P_0$ given by the theory is proportional to $\sqrt{n}$, and if plotted against $\sqrt{n}$ will give a straight line passing through the origin. For a substance like $MgSO_4$ the slope, as we have seen, will be eight times as steep as for a substance like KCl. These calculated straight lines are shown in figs. 33 and 35. The plotted ratio $(P_0 - P)/P_0$ is a measure of how far the osmotic coefficient g differs from unity; it is, in fact, equal to $(1 - g)$. Presumably no electrolyte which is partially dissociated into ions will exert a *smaller* osmotic pressure than it would if it were not dissociated at all. If this is so, the value of g for any electrolyte which furnishes a pair of ions cannot fall below $\frac{1}{2}$; that is to say, the value of $(1-g)$ will not rise above 0·5. In the same way, for electrolytes like $BaCl_2$ and $La(NO_3)_3$ which furnish 3 and 4 ions, the value of $(1-g)$ will not rise above 0·33 and 0·25 respectively. Horizontal lines at the appropriate values of $(1-g)$ have been drawn in figs. 33–35. We must expect that the experimental curve, starting at the origin with the slope calculated from (74), will bend over so as to keep below this line. In fact, we already know from (64) that the relation between $(1-g)$ and $\sqrt{n}$ will not be linear,

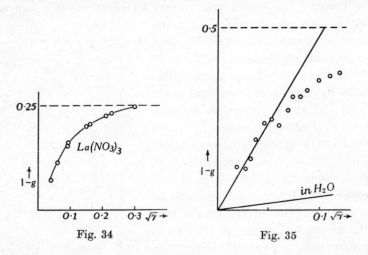

Fig. 34   Fig. 35

since at quite low concentrations the factor $(1+a/l)$ begins to differ appreciably from unity, and to make the value of the quasi-lattice energy fall below that given by (65).

It is not worth while to insert a conjectural value for a in (69), and to compare the experimental results with the values calculated from this expression, since (69) is applicable only to very dilute solutions.

We have seen that, for a substance dissolved in cyclohexanol, the initial slope of the curve should be 12·4 times the slope for the corresponding aqueous solution. The experimental results shown in fig. 35 for solutions of lithium chloride in cyclohexanol *

* Schreiner and Frivold, *Zeit. f. Phys. Chem.* **124**, 1 (1926).

lie about the theoretical line whose slope is 12·4 times the slope
for the corresponding aqueous solution.

The above description of electrolytes would hardly be accept-
able, unless one could account in a similar way for the peculiarities of their electrical conductivity, which were formerly
thought to indicate the presence of a large proportion of neutral
molecules. Debye and his collaborators showed that these
effects are to be expected even if dilute solutions are completely
dissociated into ions, and that a treatment based on expressions
(58) and (63) leads to results in agreement with experiment for
extremely dilute solutions.

CHAPTER XII

§ 1. AN ASSEMBLY OF DIPOLES

In the preceding chapters we have made continual use of the fact that the high dielectric constant of the familiar solvents depends upon the tendency of the molecular dipoles to be oriented by any electric field. But so far we have not found it necessary to examine this process in any detail. The time has now come to look more closely into the behaviour of polar dielectrics. In Chapter I it was pointed out that in fields of ordinary intensity at room temperature the amount of alignment is very small, owing to the thermal agitation. At higher temperatures the amount of orientation becomes progressively smaller, and the value of the dielectric constant decreases. For example, the dielectric constant of water has the value 88 near the freezing point, 80 at room temperature, and 55 near the normal boiling point. The value of the solvation energy of any ion in water will clearly vary with temperature.

Before considering any ion it will be better to discuss a dielectric in a uniform external field. When placed in an electrostatic field, particles possessing a permanent electric moment obey the same laws as particles possessing a permanent magnetic moment placed in a magnetic field. The treatment according to quantum theory is much simpler than the corresponding classical treatment. In classical theory a dipole or magnet placed in an external field could point in any direction, and so its energy could take up any value. In the simplest quantum theory case the energy in a field of intensity H can take only two values, namely, $-MH$ and $+MH$, where M is the permanent moment of the particle. If we plot the energy against the intensity of the field, we have the two possible states for the particle represented by two lines, like OP and OQ of fig. 36.

Consider now an assembly of similar particles, such as a gas, situated in an external field. If, starting with a certain value of H, we increase the intensity of the field, the energy of one state rises along OP by exactly the same amount as the energy of the other state falls along OQ. If, then, the population of the two states were the same, the total change of energy in the assembly would be nil. But the population of the two states is not the same; at any temperature T it is given for each

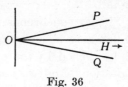

Fig. 36

state by the Boltzmann law. There are fewer particles in the upper state than in the lower. The difference in energy between the two states—the vertical distance between the lines OP and OQ—is equal to $2MH$; and the ratio of the number in the upper state to the number in the lower will be $e^{-2MH/kT}$. The stronger the field, the more will this ratio differ from unity.

At any temperature T a body possesses a certain amount of internal energy, which in the absence of a field may be called U_0. When exposed to an external field H the total internal energy will be $U = U_0 + U_H$, where U_H is that part of the internal field due to the field at that temperature. Suppose now that the body is isolated, so that no energy can flow in from outside. And suppose that, owing to some alteration which we now make in the field, the value of U_H appropriate to that temperature is increased. This increase in U_H will come about by borrowing energy from the thermal energy of the body. This means that the temperature of the body will fall. (At this lower temperature the value of U_H may be different from that at the initial temperature, in which case the body will take up a temperature reached by mutual adjustment.)

Returning to fig. 36, suppose that in a body situated in a uniform field H we have a certain distribution between the two possible states. Suppose that we reduce the intensity from H to $(H - \delta H)$. The difference in energy between the two states is diminished; hence the relative population of the two states required by the Boltzmann law is altered. In fact, there must be a greater proportion of the molecules in the upper state than before. A certain number of molecules must be raised from the lower to the upper state. The energy required to raise them is borrowed from the thermal energy, and the temperature begins to fall.

Similar conclusions result from a purely classical argument, which may be summarised here. The tendency for the dipoles to be aligned by the external field is opposed by their thermal agitation. And we must now regard this orientation as being a result of the Boltzmann law. For a dipole lying in a direction having a component along the field has a lower energy than one pointing in a direction having a component against the field. In an assembly the number of the former must by the Boltzmann factor be greater than the number of the latter; that is to say, the field has that tendency to align the dipoles with which we are so familiar. If now, the intensity of the field is reduced, the amount of alignment along the field is diminished. To turn a dipole round in the field requires a certain amount of work. The requisite energy is borrowed from the thermal energy and the temperature falls. From both arguments it follows that if the intensity of the external field is to be reduced isothermally, that is, if the temperature of the dielectric is to remain constant, heat must flow into it from outside. Conversely, if the intensity is to be increased isothermally, heat must flow out.

To throw further light on the question, we may, in passing, consider briefly the specific heat of a dielectric in an external field. The lines OP and OQ of fig. 36 are independent of temperature. If we raise the temperature of a dielectric which is situated in a constant field H, the population of the states must change; in accordance with the Boltzmann factor some molecules must be raised from the lower state to the higher. This requires energy, and the specific heat is, therefore, greater than in the absence of a field; since this is true at any temperature the integrated specific heat $\int_0^T C_p dT$ is greater than in the absence of a field.

Consider what happens if a slab of dielectric is situated in an external field, and this field is suddenly switched off. The energy in the body remains the same, but the thermal capacity is altered. Since $\int_0^T C_p dT$ is smaller in the absence of the field one might, at first sight, conclude that the temperature of the body will rise. This conclusion is wrong, for we have already seen that the temperature will fall. When H is reduced to zero some molecules are taken down along the line PO in fig. 36, but a greater number are taken up along the line QO. This requires energy, and so the temperature of the substance falls. Although the additional specific heat dU_H/dT is a positive quantity, U_H itself is a negative quantity. (By using a paramagnetic substance in a magnetic field, the behaviour has been utilised for reaching the lowest temperatures near the absolute zero. The substance is cooled as far as possible in an external magnetic field. The field is then switched off, and the temperature falls spontaneously to a temperature hitherto unattainable.)

For any assembly of dipoles in an electric field, to be able to calculate the magnitude of the thermal effects, we need to know the amount of alignment at any temperature—which is another way of saying we need to know the value of the dielectric constant at any temperature. In this chapter we have been tacitly assuming that the dipoles do not interact appreciably with one another—a condition which is realised in the case of any gas at ordinary pressures, since each molecule is so far from its neighbours that they interact only during each brief collision. For a gas we find, in agreement with observation, that the dipole part of the dielectric constant is inversely proportional to the absolute temperature. In a liquid or solid, on the other hand, the molecular dipoles are in contact all the time. Although the theory of their mutual interaction has not yet been worked out in detail, it is clear that the behaviour will at least be in the same direction as for a gas. The higher the temperature the more the thermal agitation spoils the alignment. The thermal effects on altering the intensity of the external field follow the same course as for a gas. In the absence of a quantitative theory of the alignment we can make use of experimentally determined values of the dielectric constant of the liquid. For this purpose we shall express the thermal effects directly in terms of the dielectric constant.

§ 2. IMAGE FORCES

Instead of using a uniform electric field as hitherto, we shall begin to consider a dielectric subjected to the field of a single point charge. This will serve as an introduction to the problem where we have charges of both signs present. We have already seen in Chapter I that for a charge q at a distance x from a plane dielectric the image attraction has the value

$$\left(\frac{q}{2x}\right)^2 \frac{K-1}{K+1} \qquad \ldots\ldots(75).$$

We see that the larger the value of K, the greater will be the value of this expression. Consequently the lower the temperature the larger will be the force. For a solvent at room temperature the value of K is large compared with unity, and the change in the image force is small; but we shall see later that this small change has important results.

If we plot the value of the image force against the distance x from the surface for a number of temperatures, we shall obtain a family of curves like AB and CD of fig. 37, p. 144. Each of these curves is an isothermal, and from the existence of such a set of isothermals important conclusions can immediately be drawn. The internal energy possessed by unit mass of the dielectric at temperature T depends on how far away from it the electric charge is. When the distance x is altered isothermally, heat flows out of, or into the dielectric. If this flow of heat is prevented, and an adiabatic change is made, the constant temperature cannot be maintained, and the temperature either rises or falls; i.e. there exists a family of adiabatic curves cutting the isothermals of fig. 37. Consequently from a charge and a piece of a dielectric we can construct a "heat engine". We shall move the charge away from the dielectric at a temperature T_1, doing a certain amount of work. Later, after an adiabatic step, we shall allow the charge to move towards the dielectric at a lower temperature T_2, when K is larger and the image attraction is greater. More work will be done by the engine than had been expended in the previous isothermal step, giving a balance of useful work.

Having in mind an ion above the surface of a solvent, let us suppose that a charged body is suspended by means of a spring above the surface of a dielectric, which is in contact with a heat reservoir at temperature T_1. Suppose that the tension of this spring is under our control and that we now make the tension greater by an infinitesimal amount, the charge will begin to move away from the dielectric. As it moves, a certain amount of heat flows into the dielectric to maintain the temperature. We now sever the connection with the reservoir, and make a further increase in the distance x adiabatically, fig. 37; the temperature cannot be maintained, and we let it fall to the value T_2. Placing the dielectric in contact with the reservoir at temperature T_2, we decrease the tension of the spring and allow the charge to move back towards the dielectric. If we see that the attraction never exceeds the tension of the spring by more than an infinitesimal amount, we can prevent the charge from acquiring any kinetic energy. During this step heat flows out of the dielectric, and we stop the process when we reach the particular adiabatic which passes through the initial state, fig. 37. If we now isolate the dielectric, and allow the charge to move nearer to the dielectric, the temperature rises and brings the system back to its original state.

Since a balance of useful work has been obtained, we know from the second law of thermodynamics that in this cycle a certain amount of heat must have been taken in at the higher temperature and given out at the lower temperature. Heat must have been taken in when we moved the charge away from the solvent—that is, when the dielectric was subject to a decreasing electrostatic field. We see then the connection between this treatment and that given in § 1. For our conclusion agrees with the result obtained there from a study of the orientation of the dipoles. We found that when a dielectric at any temperature is subject to a decreasing field the amount of alignment appropriate to that temperature becomes smaller. To turn any dipole round against the field requires a certain amount of energy, which is borrowed from the thermal energy; heat must therefore be taken in from outside if the temperature is to be maintained. Conversely, heat is given out when the dielectric is subject to an increasing field. In a diagram like fig. 37, the direction in which heat flows is de-

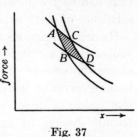

Fig. 37

termined by whether the isothermal for the higher temperature lies above or below the isothermal for the lower temperature. We see from fig. 37 that it lies below the isothermals for every lower temperature.

In the foregoing we have spoken of the charge as being outside the dielectric—that is, we have been working on the portion CE of the curve in fig. 2. We may, however, work on the portion AC of the curve; the effects will be similar since the two portions of the curve slope in the same direction. And there is no reason why, during the cycle, the ion should not be taken across the boundary of the solvent into a vacuum and back again.

§ 3. TWO CHARGES IN A DIELECTRIC

The thermal effects which we have discussed apply to any ion introduced into, or withdrawn from, a solvent. For a negative ion the effect is the same as for a positive ion. Since the changes in the intensity of the applied field are entirely due to the presence of the boundary of the dielectric, no appreciable effect will be produced by any movement of a single ion far in the interior of the solvent. A relative motion of two ions, however, is sufficient to give an effect. The case of two unlike charges is more interesting than that of like charges. Let us consider then the electrostatic field due to a pair of equal and opposite charges at a very small distance x apart. The electrostatic field of such a pair is similar to the magnetic field of a pair of magnetic poles. In the familiar expression for the field due to a small bar magnet we know that at any distant point the intensity is proportional to the moment of the magnet, i.e. is proportional to the distance between the poles. So here, if we move the charges farther apart, the intensity of the field increases in proportion to x. If the pair of charges are embedded in a polar dielectric at a certain temperature, at any point in the field the dipoles will be orientated to some extent along the direction which the field has at that point. The amount of alignment, determined by the Boltzmann law, will be proportional to the distance x between the charges. This conclusion applies only to distances large compared with x. In the very small region between the two charges the field actually becomes weaker when we move the charges farther apart; but we can easily see that the increase in the intensity in the external regions predominates. In Chapter I we made use of the fact that all electrostatic forces can be dealt with by supposing that the whole energy is stored up in the medium, and that this is true whether the medium is a vacuum or a material dielectric. To separate a pair of unlike charges we have to do work; when the charges are far apart, the energy in the medium is greater than when they are close together. This greater density of energy is due to the greater intensity of field with increasing x, which we have discussed above.

We are interested in the behaviour of the dipoles in this increasing field, when the charges are situated in a polar dielectric. Clearly, the considerations of § 1 come into force; among the dipoles the population of the states of low energy must be increased. Conversely, if we move the charges nearer together, the population of the states of high energy must be increased; some dipoles must be turned round against the field; if this is to be done isothermally, the requisite energy must be supplied from outside.

As in the previous problem the thermal effects at any temperature may be expressed directly in terms of the force of attraction between the charges. We may move them apart at a certain temperature, and later we may allow them to move together again under their mutual attraction at a higher temperature, when the value of K will be smaller and the force will be greater. A balance of useful work will have been obtained. If we plot the force y against the distance x between the ions, for two different temperatures, we shall again have a pair of curves like those of fig. 37. But whereas in fig. 37 the lower curve belonged to the higher temperature, here the isothermal for any temperature lies *above* the isothermal for any lower temperature. This is a consequence of the fact that here the dielectric is subject to an increasing field when the ions are moved farther apart (x increasing), whereas in the problem of § 2 the dielectric was subject to an increasing field when the charge was brought nearer to the surface (x decreasing). We shall again suppose that we have the ions under our control, and can move them about without allowing them to acquire an appreciable amount of kinetic energy. The internal energy of the system includes the mutual potential energy of the ions. Any change in the mutual potential energy of the ions will be equal to $\int y dx$, the work done in separating them. In any adiabatic movement of the ions this will also be the same as the change dU in the internal energy of the system.

Since the problem is somewhat complicated when the volume of the liquid v, as well as the separation x of the ions and the temperature T are taken as independent variables, we shall first write down the usual expressions for a system whose volume is not variable. When an amount of work $y dx$ is done, an amount of heat dQ flows in or out of the system. For any arbitrary reversible change of x or T

$$dU - y dx = dQ = T dS,$$

where S is the entropy of the system. As mentioned above, dU is only equal to $y dx$ in an adiabatic change. Our problem is to find the value of dU for an isothermal change; for if we allow the ions to move together freely under their own attraction, an amount of energy dU will be absorbed, or if dU is negative will be evolved as heat, and this would be susceptible to measurement by an experimentalist.

If by definition

$$A = U - TS,$$
$$dA = dU - TdS - SdT$$
$$= -SdT + ydx \qquad \ldots\ldots(76).$$

For a constant value of x, we have, putting dx equal to zero,

$$\left(\frac{\partial A}{\partial T}\right)_x = -S,$$
$$U = A - T\left(\frac{\partial A}{\partial T}\right)_x \qquad \ldots\ldots(77).$$

For an isothermal change of x, we see, putting dT in (76) equal to zero, that $dA = ydx$. Hence we obtain the result that we require:

$$dU = \left(y - T\frac{\partial y}{\partial T}\right)dx \qquad \ldots\ldots(78).$$

We may pass on now to the system where the external pressure p, or the volume v, is taken as an independent variable. The heat that will be measured calorimetrically is now not the change in U but the change in H, defined by

$$H = U + pv.$$

Corresponding to the definitions and equations above, we have now the following set of expressions,

$$dU + pdv - ydx = TdS = dQ \qquad \ldots\ldots(79),$$
$$A = H - TS$$
$$= U + pv - TS,$$
$$dA = -SdT + ydx + vdp \qquad \ldots\ldots(80).$$

Hence for constant x and constant p

$$\left(\frac{\partial A}{\partial T}\right)_{x,p} = -S,$$
$$H = U + pv = A - T\left(\frac{\partial A}{\partial T}\right)_{x,p} \qquad \ldots\ldots(81).$$

Setting both dp and dT equal to zero in (80), we see that dA is again equal to ydx. We obtain now the result that we need; for if we allow the ions to move together freely under their own attraction (in which case dx will be a negative quantity), the heat measured calorimetrically will be

$$dH = dU + pdv = \left(y - T\frac{\partial y}{\partial T}\right) dx \qquad \ldots\ldots(82).$$

If our solvent was a gas, instead of a liquid, we should not be using this thermodynamic treatment; for the heat effects in a polar gas can be calculated directly from the properties of the individual molecules. As soon as we have a satisfactory under-standing of the dielectric constants of polar liquids, we shall be able to calculate the heat effects from the molecular mechanism. In the meantime we understand the processes qualitatively, and to obtain quantitative results we have recourse to thermo-dynamics. In § 4 of the next chapter we shall make use of these expressions in studying the recombination of ions to form molecules.

CHAPTER XIII

§ 1. DISSOCIATION OF MOLECULES

In Chapter XI we discussed those solutes for which it is possible to use concentrations where the dissociation into ions is practically complete. This will occur when the mutual potential energy of the ions has a shallow minimum like that of curve a of fig. 31. But where additional forces are present due to electronic interaction between the ions, neutral molecules may persist even to the lowest concentrations that can be studied. In investigating the dissociation of molecules in solution we shall naturally wish to relate it to our knowledge of molecules in gases and vapours. But in this comparison there is a slight difficulty; for in nearly every case the molecules of a gas or vapour dissociate, not into ions, but into neutral atoms. When an ionic crystal, such as NaCl, is raised to a high temperature, it melts and finally boils; the vapour consists of diatomic molecules of NaCl. If the temperature is raised still further, these molecules begin to dissociate, not into ions, but into neutral atoms of Na and Cl.

It must be understood that this is purely a question of energy. We know that to transfer an electron from a Na atom to a distant Cl atom *in vacuo* requires work, in fact 1·3 ϵ-volts. The energy of the pair Na + Cl is lower than the energy of the pair Na$^+$ + Cl$^-$; consequently in the vapour the majority of atoms remain neutral until a higher temperature is reached. It is true that the NaCl molecule in its state of lowest energy consists of a positive and a negative ion with their electronic shells in contact. But if we consider the molecule when the nuclei are farther and farther apart, we find that the state of lowest energy is one in which the distribution of electronic charge is more and more uniform, until finally we have obtained two separate neutral atoms.

Among the alkali halides there is one for which the situation is reversed, namely caesium fluoride. Of all the elements caesium has the smallest ionisation potential, 3·87 ϵ-volts, while the energy of attachment of an electron to the fluorine atom is 4·1 ϵ-volts. When caesium fluoride is evaporated, the vapour will consist of neutral molecules, which at a still higher temperature will begin to dissociate mainly into ions. Though this behaviour is exceptional among molecules in gases, any molecule like NaCl, when introduced into a solvent, will dissociate into ions.

When such a molecule in solution is separated into a positive and a negative ion, the positive ion becomes solvated, receiving its characteristic solvation energy, and so does the negative ion. We have seen that even for a singly charged ion this solvation energy is quite large. If for any species of molecule in a certain solvent the sum of the two solvation energies $(W + W_-)$ were greater than the dissociation energy of the molecule, the state of dissociation into solvated ions would be one of lower potential energy than that of the neutral molecule; and the complete dissociation into ions at room temperature would follow. We are, therefore, led to enquire whether there is any flaw in this idea. The solvation energy of the positive ion depends upon its interaction with the adjacent solvent molecules, while that of the distant negative ion depends upon the interaction with its adjacent solvent molecules. And, since these two energies are independent, there seems at first no reason why their sum $(W + W_-)$ should not in some cases exceed, and in other cases be less than, the dissociation potential of the molecule, thus leading to the classes of electrolytes which are completely dissociated and to those which are feebly dissociated into ions in dilute solution.

By considering the solvent once more as a continuous medium with dielectric constant K, we can easily show that this cannot be so. *In vacuo* a singly charged positive ion and a negative ion attract one another with the Coulomb force ϵ^2/d^2; and in a medium of dielectric constant K they attract each other with the force ϵ^2/Kd^2. That is to say, when the ions are far apart, they do still attract one another, however feebly, and work must still be done to separate them. This is a fundamental condition, and the values of the solvation energies of the positive and negative ions, although they are independent, must in every case be such that their sum $(W + W_-)$ is not large enough to upset the condition. For every pair of unlike ions in every solvent we are right, then, in drawing a potential energy curve with a minimum, like curve a, of fig. 31. When a solute is completely dissociated into ions, this can in no case be because the curve does not possess a minimum. A similar argument must apply to the sum of the solvation energies of the ions into which any polyatomic substance like $CaCl_2$ breaks up.

§ 2. EXCHANGE FORCES

As mentioned in Chapter II, between two atoms or ions exchange forces of attraction arise when their configurations are such that one or more electrons circulate round both nuclei when these are sufficiently close together. If such a diatomic molecule is placed in a liquid, the exchange forces do not undergo the drastic change that is imposed on all electrostatic forces; the motion of the electrons is almost undisturbed. Until we have evidence to the contrary, we may take the exchange forces to be the same as in a vacuum. The important feature of these exchange forces is that they are operative only at extremely close range. For example, between two oxygen atoms the forces are inappreciable when the distance between the nuclei is greater than 3 Å. For larger atoms the limit may be 4 Å. or 5 Å., but the potential valley due to such forces is always quite narrow.

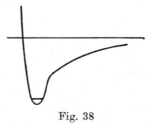

Fig. 38

We can see then what will be the shape of the potential energy for a pair of ions possessing some exchange forces of attraction in addition to the usual electrostatic forces. At a certain separation the curve will break away from the Coulomb curve downwards, as shown in fig. 38, giving a deeper and narrower bottom to the potential valley. When, as a result, the dissociation energy of the molecule is large, the degree of dissociation will be small, even in dilute solution. The electrical conductivity of a 1/50-molar solution of $HgCl_2$ in water is more than 30 times smaller than that of a substance like $MgCl_2$. This is not because the Hg^{++} ion has an abnormally low mobility; but when a Cl^- ion is brought near to a Hg^{++} ion, the supernumerary electron in the Cl^- begins to circulate round both nuclei, giving rise to a curve like fig. 38; the same must be true for a second Cl^- ion. In the crystal $HgCl_2$ does not form a simple ionic lattice, and in solution it is only feebly dissociated into ions.

§ 3. ASSOCIATED IONS

For a pair of ions in solution any point on the curves of fig. 31 represents strictly a time average of the potential energy, there being local fluctuations due to the thermal agitation of the solvent molecules. We must recognise too that, although such curves have the same form as in a vacuum, there is an obvious difference in their meaning. If we draw a horizontal line AB, to represent the total energy, fig. 39, the separation of the nuclei of the two ions varies rapidly between the values OG and OH. Take, however, a higher value of the total energy, represented by the line EF. In the case of ions in a vacuum this would mean that the separation of the ions was oscillating with high frequency

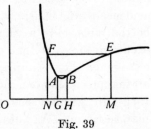

Fig. 39

between the extreme values OM and ON. In solution, on the other hand, a wide amplitude of this kind is prevented by the presence of the solvent molecules. If at any moment the ions are anything like as far apart as OM, there will be one or more solvent molecules between them, and the value of the separation will at this moment be showing only small fluctuations about the value OM. In this situation a pair of oppositely charged ions is known as a temporarily associated ion pair.

When the potential energy curve has a form like fig. 38, there is a clear distinction between a molecule where the ions are in contact and an associated ion pair where they are not. But in the absence of exchange forces there is no essential division between ions which are momentarily in contact and those which are not. In Chapter XI we were dealing with solutions so dilute that the number of associated ion pairs was negligible. In any less dilute solution the number of associated ions will depend on the form of the potential energy of the species of ions present. The behaviour of a solute possessing a curve like fig. 38 will also depend on the particular form of this curve. But even here the purely electrostatic part of the curve is common to all species of ions; and if we study how this part contributes to the behaviour of the ion, our results will be of general application. In the following sections we shall enquire how the ideas developed in the previous chapter throw light on the dissociation of such a molecule.

§ 4. HEAT OF DISSOCIATION AND RECOMBINATION

Let us first take two gaseous ions, such as Cs^+ and F^-, and study their recombination to form a neutral molecule. Starting with the ions at rest, let us release them; they move together acquiring a large amount of kinetic energy at the expense of their mutual electrostatic potential energy, the total energy remaining constant. If when they are near together they collide with a third particle the latter may take away some of this kinetic energy, with the result that Cs^+ and F^- are unable to separate. At another collision more kinetic energy may be lost, until the CsF molecule settles down in its lowest vibrational level. An amount of energy equal to the dissociation energy has been dissipated. Passing on now to ions in solution, let us watch a pair of ions which are moving towards one another. There is no essential difference from the same process in a gas. As the ions move together their mutual electrostatic potential energy is turned into kinetic energy, which is communicated to the solvent; an amount of energy equal to D is dissipated. Conversely, when a pair of ions are moving apart, they are acquiring potential energy, which is being derived from the thermal energy of the solvent.

To a physicist, who is accustomed to the idea of the dissociation energy, it comes as a surprise to find in books on electrolytes a list of heats of dissociation like Table VI, where in most cases the value given is for a heat evolved instead of for a heat absorbed. All in the list are substances which are feebly dissociated in aqueous solution; they presumably have an unusually large value of D, and are, one would have thought, the very molecules which would need heat to be supplied to dissociate them.

TABLE VI

HEAT ACCOMPANYING DISSOCIATION OF MOLECULES
INTO IONS IN AQUEOUS SOLUTION*

	Calories per gram mol
Acetic acid	300 absorbed
Dichloracetic acid	1130 evolved
Phosphoric acid	1130 ,,
Hydrofluoric acid	2570 ,,

In the preceding chapter we considered the effects accompanying the relative motion of two charges immersed in a polar medium. We deduced an expression for the heat which would be evolved if the two charges, initially at rest, were allowed to move together under their mutual attraction. We may now begin to apply this result to the recombination of a pair of singly charged ions to form a molecule. As mentioned above this subject falls naturally into two parts, the effects which are peculiar to the particular species of ions, and those which are common to all species. When the distance x between the ions is not too small, the force between them is equal or nearly equal to ϵ^2/Kx^2, the purely electrostatic force which is the same for all singly charged ions. When the ions are nearer together, the force y between them differs from this value in a way characteristic of the particular species of ions. For the total force we may then write $$y = \epsilon^2/Kx^2 + y' \qquad \ldots\ldots(83),$$

* *Treatise on Physical Chemistry*, edited by H. S. Taylor, p. 219.

where y' may be either a positive or negative quantity, which is only large for small values of x. We shall begin by paying attention to that range of x where the forces are nearly Coulomb forces. If we substitute (83) in (82), we obtain

$$dH = \frac{\epsilon^2}{x^2} \left(\frac{1}{K} - T \frac{\partial}{\partial T} \frac{1}{K} \right) dx + \left(y' - T \frac{\partial y'}{\partial T} \right) dx \quad ...(84),$$

in which we shall study the behaviour of the first bracket. In any case, if the main contribution to y' comes from exchange forces, which are independent of temperature, $\partial y'/\partial T$ will be small, and in studying the electrostatic term we shall be dealing with the most interesting part. Starting with two charges at an infinite distance apart, if we allow them to move together under their own attraction until the separation has fallen to some final value x_0, the amount of heat evolved or absorbed is obtained by integrating (84) between these limits. For simple electrostatic forces this would give

$$\frac{\epsilon^2}{x_0} \left(\frac{1}{K} - T \frac{\partial}{\partial T} \frac{1}{K} \right) \qquad ......(85).$$

In this movement the ions will have lost an amount of mutual potential energy ϵ^2/Kx_0, which has been converted into kinetic energy and dissipated as heat. The total heat evolved will differ from this by the value of the second term in (85); the heat evolved will, in fact, be smaller, since for any dielectric medium $\frac{\partial}{\partial T} \left(\frac{1}{K} \right)$ is a positive quantity. At room temperature the value of T is about 300; if then the value of $1/K$ for the medium increases by anything approaching one part in 300 per degree centigrade, the value of the second term will be comparable with the first. And the net amount of heat evolved will be quite different from the amount of potential energy converted into kinetic energy. And further, if for any medium the increase in $1/K$ is still more rapid, the second term will be larger than the first, and the evolution of heat will be replaced by a net absorption of heat. This is, as we shall see, what happens in our polar solvents. Everything will go in the opposite direction from the familiar processes in a gas. Though we are accustomed to think that heat is evolved when ions combine to form a molecule, here we see the possibility that heat must be supplied—not because the ions are repelling one another, for they are attracting—but, as we have seen, in order to carry out the disorientation of the solvent dipoles.

Near room temperature the dielectric constants of substances can be represented by

$$K = 1 + \frac{a}{T^n} \qquad \ldots \ldots (86).$$

As T increases the value of K decreases. For any polar gas theory shows that we should expect $n = 1$, and this is the behaviour found experimentally. The structure of polar liquids is not yet sufficiently understood to enable us to predict how their dielectric constant will change. It is found that K varies more rapidly with temperature than in gases. For water K is equal to 88 at the freezing point, 80 at room temperature, and 55 at normal boiling point. This can be represented by

$$K = 1 + \frac{392,000}{T^{\frac{3}{2}}} \qquad \ldots \ldots (87).$$

For values of T near room temperature a in (86) must clearly be a number large compared with T^n for every substance with a large dielectric constant. For ethyl alcohol near room temperature the value of n is 1·9.

Differentiating $1/K$ with respect to the temperature

$$\frac{d}{dT} \frac{1}{K} = -\frac{1}{K} \frac{dK}{dT} = \frac{n}{KT} \frac{a}{(a+T^n)} \qquad \ldots \ldots (88).$$

Since near room temperature T^n is small compared with a, (88) reduces to n/KT. And hence (85) takes the form

$$H = (1-n) \frac{\epsilon^2}{Kx_0} \qquad \ldots \ldots (89).$$

We see that the value of n in expression (89) is the determining factor. Whether a separation of ions of opposite sign is attended by a net evolution or absorption of heat depends on whether n

is greater or less than unity. If for any medium $n < 1$ dissipation of potential energy and evolution of heat will run parallel in the usual way. For all polar solvents, however, $n > 1$, and the effects will be in the other direction. In water, since $n = 1 \cdot 5$, the dissipation of a certain amount of potential energy will be accompanied by a net absorption of heat which is just half as large. As this expression has been obtained by treating the solvent as a continuous medium of dielectric K, it will give only qualitative results when applied to a pair of ions meeting. It appears, however, that when two charges in water move together under their own attraction, the evolution of heat is more than swamped by the absorption of heat required for the disorientation of the dipoles.

Having considered purely electrostatic forces common to all ions, we can pass on now to the formation of molecules where exchange forces contribute to the attraction. The presence of even weak exchange forces of attraction in (83) will suffice to change the sign of the heat of dissociation into ions. Heat will no longer be absorbed when the ions come together, but at least some heat will be evolved. For a certain small amount of exchange forces accompanying the usual electrostatic forces, heat will neither be evolved or absorbed, the energy of the ionic attraction being just sufficient for disorientation of the dipoles and no more. The acetic acid molecule in aqueous solution seems to approximate to this behaviour. For a molecule with stronger exchange forces more heat will be liberated when the ions combine, but we must still expect that the quantity of heat will be less than the dissociation energy by a definite amount.

§ 5. DISSOCIATION OF SOLVENT MOLECULES

For the sake of simplicity, and in order to study one thing at a time, we have hitherto been treating the solvent as far as possible as a polar medium, disregarding all properties except its dielectric constant. We have, however, sooner or later to take into account the fact that in each solvent the molecules are formed from certain particular elements in the periodic table. And this is perhaps the most convenient point to examine one direction in which these polar molecules may show characteristic behaviour.

The structure of the water molecule is shown in fig. 40. The angle between the lines joining the protons to the oxygen nucleus is about 105°. If x is the distance of one of the protons from the oxygen nucleus, and we plot the potential energy of the molecule against x, we shall have a curve of the usual form; the equilibrium distance is about 1·0 Å. The large dipole moment of the molecule is due to the fact that the electronic density round the oxygen core is larger than is required to neutralise the positive charge of the core, while round the protons it is insufficient to neutralise

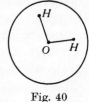

Fig. 40

their charge. The same is true of the protons in the NH_3 molecule, while in the CH_3OH molecule and in each of the other alcohols the non-uniformity of charge is in the OH group, the negative charge being again round the oxygen.

Consider now any particular molecule in the interior of one of these liquids. If the positive and negative parts of the dipole become separated, two solvated ions will be formed. The question is how great is the work D which must be done to dissociate the molecule in this way. For if in any liquid D is not too large, there will be at room temperature, in accordance with Boltzmann's law, an appreciable number of solvent molecules dissociated into ions. For none of the familiar solvents can the value of D be small—as we shall see, certainly not as small as half an electron-volt—otherwise the pure liquid would be a good conductor. On the other hand, when D is large, the number of ions at room temperature will be below the limit of detection. In practice the difficulty of tracing a minute amount of self-ionisation in any liquid arises from the difficulty of obtaining it sufficiently free from impurities.

Water is the solvent to which most attention has been given. After 42 successive distillations Kohlrausch and Heydweiller obtained a specimen of water with the lowest conductivity on record, namely $4 \cdot 3 \times 10^{-8}$ reciprocal ohms per cm.[3] at 18° C. The conductivity appeared to be approaching a fairly definite limit, ascribed to the dissociation of water into hydrogen and hydroxyl ions, and having a value estimated at $3 \cdot 77 \times 10^{-8}$ reciprocal ohms per cm.[3] The actual number of ions which this small conductivity represents can at once be calculated by direct comparison with aqueous solutions of substances furnishing hydrogen and hydroxyl ions. The number of ion pairs in pure water at room temperature is found to be in the neighbourhood of 5×10^{13} per cm.[3] Since the number of water molecules in one cm.[3] is $3 \cdot 6 \times 10^{22}$, the fraction α of these molecules dissociated into ions is $1 \cdot 4 \times 10^{-9}$. Since each species of molecule has its own characteristic value of D, there is no reason why other solvents should show anything like the same amount of self-dissociation.

In interpreting this value of α there are two important points to be taken into account. In general, the dissociation of a substance depends, according to (8), upon the volume v in which it is contained. If a small quantity of one liquid, say water, is introduced into a large volume of another solvent, the water molecules will behave as particles of a solute, and their degree of dissociation into ions will depend on their concentration. On the other hand, in the self-dissociation of a solvent, which is under discussion here, the position is different, since the volume of the liquid is pre-determined. In the second place, whereas the dissociation of a substance usually means an increase in the number of particles, the dissociation of water is more correctly represented by

$$2H_2O \rightleftharpoons (H_3O)^+ + (OH)^- \qquad \ldots\ldots(90),$$

where the number of particles remains the same, a proton being simply transferred from one water molecule to another. Just as in the water molecule itself the two protons lie within the general electron cloud, fig. 40, so will all three protons within the $(H_3O)^+$ ion. And in the other common solvents which contain hydrogen the mode of dissociation is presumably by a similar protonic transition

$$2NH_3 \rightleftharpoons (NH_4)^+ + (NH_2)^- \qquad \text{......(91)},$$
$$2(CH_3OH) \rightleftharpoons (CH_3OH_2)^+ + (CH_3O)^- \qquad \text{......(92)}.$$

The number of protons transferred is the number of molecules dissociated. In each case the volume v drops out of (8), and the constant A will scarcely differ from unity. For water at room temperature, from the observed value of α we estimate that the value of the dissociation energy D lies in the neighbourhood of $1 \cdot 0$ ϵ-volt. This includes first, the work to transfer a proton from a molecule to its neighbour, and secondly, the electrostatic work to separate these ions against their attraction; the potential energy curve will be like fig. 38. For water we have accurate information about the heat accompanying recombination of the ions; this will be dealt with in the next section.

§ 6. RECOMBINATION OF IONS TO FORM SOLVENT MOLECULES

Let us first consider solutes of various kinds dissolved in different solvents. We can divide the solutions into two classes—those where the solute contains no atom of a species already present in the solvent molecule, and those where the solute does contain an atom or group of atoms present in the solvent molecule. Consider for example a solute containing nitrogen but not hydrogen or oxygen; it would belong to the second class when dissolved in liquid NH_3, but to the first class when dissolved in water. Among the second class the most important are those where part of the solute molecule is identical with either the positive or the negative half of the solvent dipole—where the solute on dissociating furnishes one or other of the ions which is formed, or would be formed, when the solvent molecule itself dissociates. For example, ammonium bromide dissolved in liquid ammonia dissociates partially into NH_4^+ and Br^-, while sodium amide in the same solvent dissociates partially into Na^+ and NH_2^-. If we were to mix these two solutions, two of the species of ions can disappear to form solvent molecules by (91).

The importance of this disappearance of ions to form solvent molecules has long been recognised in aqueous solutions, and is known as the neutralisation of an acid by a base. In dilute aqueous solution a strong acid HX is completely dissociated into ions $(H_3O)^+$ and X^-, while a dilute solution of a strong base MOH is dissociated into M^+ and $(OH)^-$. If we mix two equivalent solutions, two species of ions will combine to form solvent molecules:

$$M^+ + (OH)^- + (H_3O)^+ + X^- \rightarrow M^+ + X^- + 2H_2O \quad ......(93).$$

Of the four species of ions two remain unchanged, and might have been omitted from (93), the reaction being merely (90). If any heat is evolved or absorbed, this will be just the heat of recombination of the solvated hydrogen and hydroxyl ions to form water molecules. We should find then that in very dilute aqueous solution the heats of neutralisation of various strong acids by strong bases have one and the same value. In less

TABLE VII

HEAT OF NEUTRALISATION OF NaOH IN AQUEOUS SOLUTION WITH VARIOUS ACIDS AT 20° C. IN CALORIES EVOLVED PER MOL*

Dilution in mols H_2O	$100 + 100$	$200 + 200$	$400 + 400$	Infinite
HCl	13,924	13,854	13,794	13,640 cals†
HBr	13,856	—	—	—
HI	13,797	—	—	—
HNO_3	13,850	13,804	13,769	13,640 cals†

dilute solution the values will differ slightly, depending upon the particular values of the configuration energies of the solutions used. The experimental values given in Table VII show that in the formation of water molecules the recombination of ions is accompanied by a considerable evolution of heat. For both HCl and HNO_3 the limit found by extrapolation to infinite

* Richards and Hall, *J. Amer. Chem. Soc.* **51**, 735 (1929).
† Or 0.592 ϵ-volt.

dilution is $0 \cdot 592$ ϵ-volt per ion pair, or 13,640 calories per mol. This, as we expect, is considerably smaller than the estimate made above for the dissociation energy. When the hydrogen and hydroxyl ions combine to form neutral molecules, the surrounding liquid is subject to a decreasing electrostatic field, and a certain amount of energy must be taken up by the polar molecules to maintain the temperature constant.

CHAPTER XIV

§ 1. THE EVALUATION OF Y

In the foregoing chapters we have found that the behaviour of ions in solution may be understood in terms of the characteristic energies W, Y, $_mJ_{m'}$, D, and so on. In working out the relations between these various quantities, we have had all along a rough idea of their orders of magnitude. In the opening chapter we made an estimate of the solvation energy of ions in various stages of ionisation. We found that for a singly charged positive or negative ion the value would be 3 or 4 ϵ-volts, and for doubly charged ions between 12 and 30 ϵ-volts. In the second place we saw that when Y is equal to or less than W, a positive core can pass easily from a metallic surface into solution without the assistance of an electrical double layer. Further, we have seen how the values of J and D in any solvent depend on that of W.

But this analysis has brought us only half-way towards our goal. For each species of ion has its own characteristic value of W and J, and each metal has its own characteristic value of Y and ϕ. It is only when we evaluate for each ion the characteristic energies that we obtain a detailed picture of the individual behaviour of each species. Our aim in the remaining chapters of this volume will be, not only to fill in their numerical values, but also to make use of these. It is only when one has made oneself thoroughly familiar with the values, at least of some of the commoner ions, that one begins to have a clear mental picture of the various ionic processes.

Let us begin with the quantity Y, the work required to remove a positive core from the surface of a metal into a vacuum. We can evaluate this in terms of known quantities by means of a cycle. Consider a positive core on the surface of the lattice of a monovalent metal, like silver; let the core be vibrating in its lowest level AB in fig. 41. We can remove this core from the metal either with or without an electron. When we remove a

neutral atom, we do work equal to the sublimation energy S.
Let the curve ABE represent the potential energy in this process, the depth of the valley being S. Having now a free atom,
let us ionise it, doing work $\mathscr{I}$, and then replace the electron in
the metal, receiving energy ϕ. For
every monovalent metal the value of $\mathscr{I}$
is greater than ϕ; the net work done
in this step is $(\mathscr{I}-\phi)$. If we now bring
the positive core back to its original
position on the lattice, it will participate fully in the free electrons, and

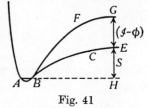

Fig. 41

we shall have returned to our initial state; the cycle will be
complete. As we bring back the ion to the metal, it is attracted,
and falls into its former level AB. During this process the
potential energy of the system is to be represented by a curve
like $GFBA$, the energy represented by the vertical distance GE
being equal to $(\mathscr{I}-\phi)$, as explained above; the work required
to remove a positive core into a vacuum is greater by this amount
than the work to remove a neutral atom, for clearly the height
of FG above AB is just the quantity Y. For every monovalent
metal

$$Y = \mathscr{I}-\phi+S \qquad \ldots\ldots(94).$$

Take for example silver. The electronic work function has been
measured with great care, and found to be 4·74 ϵ-volts; the
sublimation energy is 2·9 ϵ-volts, and the first ionisation potential *in vacuo* 7·53 ϵ-volts. We find then that the work to remove
a singly charged positive core from the surface of silver is
$(7·53-4·74+2·9)=5·7$ ϵ-volts. In the same way we can find
the value of Y for any monovalent metal when the other three
quantities are known.

If we go on now to study metals of higher valency we shall
have to use the symbol Y_1 to denote the quantity we have been
calling Y. For in addition to Y_1 we shall be interested in the
work Y_2 to obtain a doubly charged ion, and Y_3 for a trebly
charged ion. The values of these quantities can be obtained by
means of a cycle similar to the last. Having taken a neutral

atom from the surface into a vacuum, we can remove either two or three electrons from it, doing work either $_0\mathscr{I}_2$ or $_0\mathscr{I}_3$. On putting the electrons back into the metal, we receive energy 2ϕ or 3ϕ. Thus in general

$$Y_m = {_0\mathscr{I}_m} - m\phi + S \qquad \ldots\ldots(95).$$

As an example let us evaluate Y_2 for cobalt. The electronic work function is $4\cdot1$ ϵ-volts (see Table XIV) and the sublimation energy is $3\cdot7$ ϵ-volts. We see from Table XI that the work to remove two electrons from the neutral cobalt atom amounts to $25\cdot8$ ϵ-volts. We find then $Y_2 = (25\cdot8 - 8\cdot2 + 3\cdot7) = 21\cdot3$ ϵ-volts. For few metals is the value of the work function ϕ known to within $0\cdot1$ ϵ-volt, though measurements with modern technique are being extended to the remaining metals. A few of the more reliable values have been given in Table XIV. To obtain a working knowledge of ionic mechanisms it is not necessary at the moment to have accurate values of Y_m for all the metals, though these will doubtless become available in course of time.

A similar attitude may be taken with regard to values of the solvation energies of ions. Although we may hope that accurate values of W for every ion in each of the common solvents will ultimately be obtained, it is more important at the moment to learn how to handle the solvation energies, even if the values are uncertain to more than $0\cdot1$ ϵ-volt. Many factors influence the solvation energy of an ion but the approximate evaluation of a solvation energy from the relevant experimental data rests upon an extremely straightforward argument. Although in § 2, for the sake of completeness, we give a discussion of the various factors, it is important that these details should not be allowed to obscure the simple argument by which the value of any solvation energy in aqueous solution can be obtained correct to within a few per cent.

§ 2. SOLVATION ENERGY AND HEAT OF SOLVATION

Equations (79) to (82) were true for both the problems which we began to study in Chapter XII. So far we have been developing their application to the relative motion of two ions. We may now go back to the earlier problem where y was the force acting on a single ion crossing the boundary of a solvent at any given temperature. By definition the solvation energy of the ion at that temperature is given by $\int y\,dx$, where the integral is taken from $-\infty$ to ∞, or between any two points sufficiently far from the boundary on either side. In Chapter I it was pointed out that if an ion were held at rest near the surface of a solvent, and released, it would be accelerated into the liquid and would acquire kinetic energy equal at any distance x to the vertical distance between the two lines of fig. 2—that is, equal to the potential energy $\int y\,dx$ which has been lost. Through collisions with solvent molecules this kinetic energy would be dissipated as heat. But we know that the heat of solvation is not equal to this solvation energy. For in Chapter XII we again considered the bringing of a charge towards the surface of a solvent —this time infinitely slowly; the whole of the potential energy was made to do work, and none was converted into kinetic energy. We found that, because the medium was subject to an increasing electric field, there would still be a small but definite amount of heat evolved.

In the solvation of an ion these two heating effects are additive; they are of the same sign, since, when y is an image force, $\partial y/\partial T$ is negative. They are given respectively by the two terms in the following expressions, derived from (82):

$$\int y\,dx - \int T\,\frac{\partial y}{\partial T}\,dx = W - T\,\frac{\partial W}{\partial T} \qquad \ldots\ldots(96).$$

The relative magnitude of the two terms may be estimated by using (4) and (89), and taking a to be independent of temperature:

$$(1 - 1/K)\,\epsilon^2/2a - T\,\frac{\partial}{\partial T}\,(1 - 1/K)\,\epsilon^2/2a = \frac{\epsilon^2}{2a}\left(1 - \frac{1}{K} + \frac{n}{K}\right)$$
$$\ldots\ldots(97).$$

The heat differs from the solvation energy by the presence of the term n/k. For ethyl alcohol, as we have seen, $n = 1\cdot9$, and $K = 26$ at room temperature. Hence, if (97) gives the correct magnitude, the heat of solvation of a single ion in ethyl alcohol differs from its solvation energy by more than 7 per cent. For water at room temperature $n = 1.5$ and $K = 80$, hence the two quantities will differ by less than 2 per cent. Nevertheless this difference is large enough to be responsible for the peculiarities of the heat of dissociation of molecules in aqueous solution.

We have so far been using the term "heat of solvation" rather loosely. We have supposed that an ion initially at rest in a vacuum is plunged into a solvent at temperature T. Of the energy liberated the ion will retain a certain amount, $3kT$, as its own thermal energy appropriate to the temperature T. If by the heat of solvation we mean the heat which would be measured in an imaginary calorimetric experiment, this heat retained by the ion must first be subtracted. At room temperature $3kT$ is 0.075 ϵ-volt, which amounts to about 2 per cent. of the heat of solvation for a singly charged ion. In comparing the heat of solvation with the solvation energy for singly charged ions in aqueous solution, this roughly cancels out the 2 per cent. difference which was mentioned in the last paragraph; and, in the present state of our knowledge, there is no need to tabulate separate values of the heat of solvation and the solvation energy. For doubly charged ions, however, there is still an appreciable difference between the numerical values of the two quantities.

§3. HEAT OF SOLUTION OF IONIC CRYSTAL

This introduction of an ion into a solvent from a vacuum is an artificial process, but the same arguments may be applied to the passage of ions into solution from the surface of a crystal. As the solution of a salt crystal is a process which has not yet been touched on in this book, it will be better, before approaching the thermal effects, to look into the general features, beginning with uni-univalent substances. The solution of such a salt crystal is not unlike the dissociation of neutral molecules into pairs of ions. In the latter process we receive energy $(W + W_-)$ after doing work per molecule equal to D. In the solution of the crystal we again receive energy $(W + W_-)$, having done work equal to the lattice energy per ion pair. In the case of a substance of higher valency we have a group of ions, whose solvation energies may add up to 20 or 30 ϵ-volts. We are interested in the amount by which the sum of these solvation energies will differ from the value of the lattice energy of the crystal. There seems to be room for considerable divergence, as each of the ions becomes solvated separately. We shall find, however, that there is actually very little latitude. In the first place, it was shown at the end of Chapter I that a good estimate of the lattice energy is obtained by supposing that each ion present in the crystal contributes a term $\frac{m^2\epsilon^2}{2a}\,(1-1/K)$, where K is the dielectric constant of the crystal, and a the radius of the volume occupied by the ion in the crystal. But a good estimate of the solvation energy of each ion is, of course, obtained by a similar expression containing the dielectric constant of the solvent and the radius of the volume occupied by the ion in the solvent, which is nearly the same as that occupied in the crystal. We see then why the solvation energies of the various ions add up to a value not very different from the lattice energy, and why no large amount of energy is liberated, even in cases where the lattice energy amounts to 20 or 30 ϵ-volts. When an ionic crystal is insoluble or very sparingly soluble in a certain solvent, it is because the sum of the solvation energies of the ions in this particular solvent is considerably less than the lattice energy.

We may now begin to study the thermal effects by supposing that one surface of such a crystal is in contact with a polar medium of dielectric constant K. Let us fix attention on one particular ion which is a member of the surface layer of the lattice. If we begin to remove this ion into the solvent, we find that the electrostatic force of attraction between the ion and the surface is smaller than in a vacuum by a factor which depends slightly on the temperature of the medium. When the ion is at a distance x from the surface, let the value of this force be y when the temperature is T. The higher the temperature the larger is y, since the lattice energy of the crystal is practically independent of temperature, while the dielectric constant of the solvent decreases with increasing T. On plotting y against x, we again have a set of isothermals, as in fig. 37, accompanied by a set of adiabatics; and all the results of Chapter XII apply here. If we replace the ion on the surface at the lattice-point from which we took it, we receive back energy equal to the work which we did in removing it. But at the same time the polar medium is subject to a decreasing field, and the energy needed for disorientation of the dipoles is borrowed from the thermal energy of the medium. If this amount of heat absorbed is greater than the amount of potential energy dissipated, the *heat* of solution may be of opposite sign from the *energy* of solution, as in the case of heats of dissociation.

These considerations are not only of theoretical interest, but they must also form the basis of any precise determination of the heats of solvation of ions from experimental data. If we fix attention on a pair of ions lying on the surface of a crystal like NaCl, we can either take them into solution directly, or we can take them into a vacuum, and then plunge them into solution—a cycle devised by Fajans*. Just as the amount of work must be the same by either route, so must the amount of heat evolved or absorbed be the same by either route. The heat of solution of the crystal in a particular solvent at temperature T must be equal to the algebraic sum of two quantities, the lattice heat and the heat of solvation—that is to say, (a) the amount of heat which must be supplied to the crystal at temperature T to break it up into its ions and leave them in a vacuum at long distances apart in a certain state, and (b) the amount of heat when we bring the ions from this intermediate state into the solvent at the same temperature T.

In the intermediate state we can either take the ions to be at rest, or to possess kinetic energy appropriate to the initial and final temperature T. The value which we shall give to the heat of solvation of ions will depend on our definition, which

* *Verh. d. Deutsch. Phys. Ges.* **21**, 709 (1919).

we shall choose merely from considerations of convenience. The values of lattice energies and lattice heats which one finds tabulated in the literature are all for ions left at rest. In order to use these tables it is convenient to define the heat of solvation as being for ions initially at rest in a vacuum, and finally in a solvent at temperature T and possessing the thermal energy appropriate to this temperature.

§ 4. EVALUATION OF SOLVATION ENERGIES

It is clear that the statements made at the end of § 1 are correct. If we are wanting only approximate values of solvation energies, these are connected with the lattice energy by an extremely simple relation; but if we want more exact values, there are a number of considerations to be made. As use is to be made of the heats of solution of crystalline salts, it was at any rate desirable that the relation between a heat of solution and the corresponding energy of solution should be clearly understood. We may now proceed to deal with the experimental data for ions in aqueous solution at room temperature, some of which are given in Table XII.

As an illustration let us take the substance potassium fluoride in water as solvent. It is found that when KF dissolves in water at room temperature heat is evolved. From the observed values we find by extrapolation that the heat of solution at infinite dilution will be 0·18 ϵ-volt per ion pair, or 4·1 kcal. per mol. The lattice heat of KF at room temperature is 8·13 ϵ-volts or 187·5 kcal. per mol. Adding these together, we find that the heats of solvation of the ions K$^+$ and F$^-$ in water at room temperature must together amount to 8·3 ϵ-volts per ion pair or 192 kcal. per mol. We see that the estimate which we made in Chapter I for the solvation energy of singly charged ions is in agreement with this experimental value.

In selecting the substance KF as an example, we did so for a special purpose, for the empirical radii ascribed to the ions K$^+$ and F$^-$ by crystallographers are almost identical. If the heat of solvation of an ion depends only on the magnitude of its charge and its radius, the heats of solvation of the ions K^+ and F^- in any solvent must be almost identical. For ions in aqueous solution Bernal and Fowler* have put forward the view that, owing to the peculiar structure of water molecules, the heat of solvation of a negative ion will be some two per cent. greater than for a positive ion of the same radius. We may, therefore, divide the 8·3 ϵ-volts into two nearly equal halves, and obtain for K^+ the value 4·1 ϵ-volts, and for F^- the value 4·2 ϵ-volts. When in course of time we have more detailed information about ions in solution, we shall be able to check the accuracy of these values.

The negative ion of iodine, being larger than F^-, will have a smaller heat of solvation. From the lattice heat and heat of solution of crystalline potassium iodide we find that the heats of solvation of K^+ and I^- together amount to 6·2 ϵ-volts. Using the value 4·1 ϵ-volts already obtained for K^+ we find for I^- at room temperature the value 2·1 ϵ-volts. In the same way we obtain for the bromine negative ion in aqueous solution the value 2·5, and for chlorine 2·8 ϵ-volts. Proceeding from here to the chlorides of other elements, we can obtain the heat of solvation in water of every metallic ion for whose chloride the lattice energy and heat of solution are known.

As the knowledge of the lattice energy of a crystal is the first requisite towards determining the solvation energy of its ions, we shall give a brief outline of the methods by which the values are obtained. It has already been mentioned in Chapter III that for very simple ionic crystals, like rock salt, the electrostatic energy is known; the repulsive forces and van der Waals' forces having been calculated by the methods of quantum mechanics, values of the lattice energy are obtained, which are believed to be very accurate. For most crystals the lattice energy is obtained in terms of other experimentally measured quantities by means of a cycle devised by Born, similar to that by which we obtained values of Y. Owing to an uncertainty about one of the quantities which occurs in this cycle (namely, the energy

* *J. Chem. Phys.* 1, 535 (1933).

of attachment of an electron to any halogen atom), this experimental cycle had first to be checked by comparing the values which it gives for simple crystals with the values obtained by the other method.

For most metallic elements the heat liberated when a quantity of the solid metal at room temperature combines chemically with chlorine, or other halogen, is known. The main idea of the Born cycle is to make use of this chemical heat of formation to deduce the lattice energy of the resulting crystalline compound. The lattice energy is the work required to split the compound into its constituent ions. If, having done this, we transfer the electrons from the negative ions to the positives, and then allow these neutral substances to combine chemically, we get back to the crystal from which we started. This cycle is carried out by the following nine steps:

(1) Starting with the crystal (a halide) at room temperature, we abstract heat from it until it reaches the absolute zero.

(2) We split the crystal into free ions at rest in a vacuum.

(3) We remove the supernumerary electrons from the negative ions, and

(4) transfer them to the positive ions.

(5) We allow the halogen atoms to combine to form diatomic molecules, still at rest in a vacuum, and then

(6) bring this gas to room temperature at atmospheric pressure.

(7) We bring the metallic vapour up to room temperature, and

(8) condense the vapour to form solid metal.

(9) We allow chemical combination to take place.

To make comparisons between the lattice energies of different substances it is unnecessary to know all the steps in the cycle. For example, we can find the difference between the lattice energy of $AgNO_3$ and that of KNO_3 without knowing the energies for the NO_3 radical or ion. Using this method we find that the heat of solvation of the Ag^+ ion is nearly 1·4 ϵ-volts greater than that of K^+—that is to say, 5·5 ϵ-volts.

This value is of particular interest since at the beginning of this chapter we deduced the value of Y for Ag; using the observed value of ϕ we found the value of Y to be 5·7 ϵ-volts. We see then that for silver the values of Y and W in aqueous solution are nearly the same. Recalling that it is the value of $(Y - W)$ which determines the strength of the double layer for equilibrium at a soluble electrode, we conclude that when a piece of silver is dipped into an aqueous solution containing Ag$^+$ ions at a moderate concentration, only an extremely weak electrical double layer will be present at the interface.

§ 5. THE ENERGIES OF ELECTRONIC LEVELS

Having obtained numerical values of the solvation energies, we can at once find the positions of the electronic levels in positive and negative solvated ions. The first ionisation potential of the silver atom *in vacuo* is 7·53 ϵ-volts. In solution it will be

$$\mathscr{I} - W = 7·5 - 5·5 = 2·0 \ \epsilon\text{-volts.}$$

For all singly charged positive ions in aqueous solution the value of $(\mathscr{I} - W)$ is remarkably small.

Although the procedure of the last paragraph sounds quite logical, it should be pointed out that the determination really is made in the opposite direction. In the step (4) of the Born cycle given above the value of $\mathscr{I}$ has already been used. In fact, for any positive ion the Born cycle really gives us the value of $(\mathscr{I} - W)$, and it is by inserting the known value of $\mathscr{I}$ that we find W. With regard to the silver ion, it might more explicitly have been stated that, by a comparison with K$^+$, we find that for Ag$^+$ the value of $(\mathscr{I} - W)$ is 2·0 ϵ-volts, and hence the value of W is $7·5 - 2·0 = 5·5$ ϵ-volts. When the value of any required $_m\mathscr{I}_{m'}$ *in vacuo* is not yet known, as is the case for $_2\mathscr{I}_3$ of both Fe and Cr, the corresponding $_mW_{m'}$ cannot yet be determined.

By adding the values of W_- to those of $\mathscr{I}_-$, the values of J_- for each of the halogen negative ions are at once found. For

I⁻, Br⁻, and Cl⁻, we find that $(\mathscr{I}_- + W_-)$ has the values 5·3, 6·1, and 6·6 ϵ-volts, respectively. It might be thought that we could at once use these values to discuss the compatibility of positive and negative ions—to determine the species of positive ions which can co-exist with each of the halogen ions, by comparing the energies of their vacant levels with the above values. We shall see, however, that in the case of the halogen ions an additional factor must be taken into account.

Let us consider in greater detail what we mean by the ionisation potential of an ion in dilute solution. By the ionisation potential of the atomic negative ion X⁻ we mean the work required to remove the supernumerary electron and to leave the neutral atom X among solvent molecules, as it normally is in dilute solution. But consider now the situation if there happens to be another identical neutral atom X nearby, and if the element X is one which can form a diatomic molecule X_2. We know that if we have two bromine atoms, or two iodine atoms, and if we plot the potential energy of the pair against their distance apart, we shall have a curve like that of fig. 42, the depth of the minimum being the dissociation potential D of the diatomic molecule Br_2, or I_2, in solution.

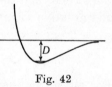

Fig. 42

When we say that the work required to remove the supernumerary electron from any negative ion X⁻ is equal to $(\mathscr{I}_- + W_-)$, we assume that we are leaving the neutral atom in a state whose energy corresponds to the horizontal line in fig. 42. But it is clear that if there happens to be another neutral atom X nearby, at a distance represented by some point in fig. 42, the neutral atom may be left in a state of lower energy given by the distance of the curve below the axis. In this case the work required to remove the electron from the negative ion will have been less than normal, because the extra energy liberated during the process will have supplied some of the amount. When two negative ions are far apart, the total work required to remove an electron from each is twice $(\mathscr{I}_- + W_-)$.

When they are near together, the total work may be less than

$$2 (\mathscr{I}_- + W_-),$$

but cannot be less than

$$\{2 (\mathscr{I}_- + W_-) - D\}.$$

Thus the work per ion, that is to say the ionisation potential, may be less than $(\mathscr{I}_- + W_-)$, but cannot be less than

$$(\mathscr{I}_- + W_- - \tfrac{1}{2}D) \qquad \ldots\ldots(98).$$

Suppose that we mix a solution containing a species of ion A^{++} with a solution containing bromine or iodine ions; and suppose that the vacant electronic level of this positive ion is about half an ϵ-volt higher than the normal position of the occupied level of the negative ion. Even in this case a positive ion is not immune from invasion by an electron, because, as we have seen, under exceptional circumstances, the occupied level of the negative ion may become momentarily higher. It is true that every negative ion may make millions of encounters with the A^{++} ions, without transferring its electron. But since in a solution of moderate concentration each ion will make at least 10^{10} collisions per second with ions of opposite sign, it is clear that, even if only a fraction 10^{-10} of the encounters are effective, the reaction will take place almost instantaneously. If we were discussing rates of reaction, we should have to estimate the number of effective collisions. But here we are interested only in the final result. To determine this, we have simply to compare the vacant level of the positive ion, not with the normal $J_- = \mathscr{I}_- + W_-$, but with the most favourable value, which we may call J'_-, and which is given by $(\mathscr{I}_- + W_- - \tfrac{1}{2}D)$. For the halogen ions the values are listed in Table VIII.

TABLE VIII

	$\mathscr{I}_- + W_-$	$\tfrac{1}{2}D$	J'_-
Iodine	5·3	0·77	4·5 ϵ-volts
Bromine	6·1	0·98	5·1 ,,
Chlorine	6·6	1·23	5·4 ,,
Fluorine	8·3	1·37	6·9 ,,

For multiply charged positive ions, such as Fe^{+++}, a similar question does not arise, since ions like Fe^{++} formed from them by capture of an electron have no tendency to stick together. In discussing their electronic levels there is no value to be taken into account other than the usual $_mJ_{m'}$.

We can now begin to examine in detail the question of the species of ions which can co-exist in aqueous solution, and those which cannot. It is clear that if a particle has a vacant level lying between 4·5 and 5·1 ϵ-volts, it can exist in the presence of the bromine ion, but will capture an electron from the iodine ion. When, for example, a dilute solution of a ferric salt is mixed with an equivalent solution of potassium iodide, most of the ferric ions capture electrons and remain in solution as Fe^{++}, and neutral iodine is liberated.* Ferric bromide, on the other hand, is stable in aqueous solution, and will crystallise out in the form of a hydrate.

We can, therefore, begin by placing the ionisation potential $_2J_3$ for Fe somewhere between 4·5 and 5·1 ϵ-volts. And this enables us to fix roughly the positions of the electronic levels of the other ions in Table IV. It is clear that the values must run from less than 4 ϵ-volts for chromium to nearly 6 ϵ-volts for cobalt. The ions of Ce and Co, which have deeper vacant levels, will capture electrons not only from the iodine ion but from the bromine ion also, and perhaps from the chlorine ion as well.

For none of the elements in Table IV have we the necessary data for evaluating $_mW_{m'}$ from the Born cycle. In the case of titanium the ionisation potentials *in vacuo* are known accurately, but not the heats of formation and solution. For iron and chromium the heats of formation and solution are known, but not the third ionisation potential. Nevertheless we can find the value $_2J_3$ for Fe and Cr. When dealing with singly charged ions, we pointed out that the Born cycle gives us the value of $(\mathscr{I} - W)$

---

* For the behaviour of substances mentioned in the following chapters see Mellor, *Comprehensive Treatise on Inorganic Chemistry*, and Abegg, *Handbuch der anorganischen Chemie*.

directly, even if the value of $\mathscr{I}$ is unknown. The same applies to multiply charged ions; the cycle gives us $(_m\mathscr{I}_{m'} - _mW_{m'})$ directly, even when $_m\mathscr{I}_{m'}$ is unknown. We can thus find the position of the vacant electronic level in the solvated Fe^{+++} ion. According to the International Critical Tables the heats of formation and solution of $FeCl_2$ together amount to 4·33 ϵ-volts, while those of $FeCl_3$ amount to 5·56 ϵ-volts. In the latter one more chlorine is involved, and hence an additional $(\mathscr{I}_- + W_- - \frac{1}{2}D)$ comes into the cycle. The change in the heat of solvation belonging to the change from Fe^{++} to Fe^{+++} is thus

$$(5\cdot56 - 4\cdot33 - 5\cdot4 + _2\mathscr{I}_3) = (_2\mathscr{I}_3 - 4\cdot2) \ \epsilon\text{-volts} \quad \ldots\ldots(99).$$

The third ionisation potential of Fe *in vacuo* is believed to be in the neighbourhood of 34 ϵ-volts. The value of (99) is thus about 29 or 30 ϵ-volts. To obtain the change in the solvation energy* we have to subtract the usual 2 per cent., or 0·6 ϵ-volt. The approximate value of $_2\mathscr{I}_3$ has only been mentioned in order to make this step clear. The value of $_2J_3$ is obtained direct from (99), as

$$_2J_3 = (4\cdot2 + 0\cdot6) = 4\cdot8 \ \epsilon\text{-volts} \quad \ldots\ldots(100).$$

We find, then, that the vacant level of Fe^{+++} lies, as it should, in a position to capture an electron from the iodine ion, but not from the bromine ion in aqueous solution.

If we take from the International Critical Tables the corresponding values for $CrCl_2$ and $CrCl_3$, namely, 5·13 and 7·37 ϵ-volts, we find that the change in the heat of solvation is $(_2\mathscr{I}_3 - 3\cdot2)$. For the third ionisation potential of chromium Landolt and Börnstein's Tables suggest 27 ϵ-volts as a provisional value. This would put the value of $_2W_3$ between 23 and 24 ϵ-volts, and 2 per cent. of this amounts to 0·47 ϵ-volt. We thus find for chromium:

$$_2J_3 = (3\cdot2 + 0\cdot47) = 3\cdot67 \ \epsilon\text{-volts} \quad \ldots\ldots(101).$$

The vacant level of the solvated Cr^{+++} ion turns out to be rather more than 1·1 ϵ-volts higher than that of Fe^{+++}. This is in excellent agreement with our interpretation of Table IV in

* See p. 167.

Chapter x. The standard electrode potential given there for chromium is 1·14 ϵ-volts negative with respect to that for iron; and this, we saw, could only mean that the electronic level is higher by this amount.

Using our values for Cr and Fe, we can now convert Table IV into a table of electronic levels.

TABLE IX

		ϵ-volts
Cr	$_2J_3$	3·67
Ti	,,	4·4
Fe	,,	4·8
Ce	$_3J_4$	5·6
Co	$_2J_3$	5·9

These values, together with the values of J'_- for the halogen ions, are shown in fig. 43 on page 189, the occupied levels being indicated on the left and the vacant levels on the right.

When we consider Table IX as a whole, we notice that all the values lie within a narrow range of energy whose limits are 3·6 and 5·9 ϵ-volts. Among the metals which exist in aqueous solution in two successive stages of ionisation, m and $m+1$, there is none known having the value of J that lies outside this range. When we recall that among the ionisation potentials and solvation energies which together determine the J are values ranging from 20 to 40 ϵ-volts, it is at first sight remarkable that all the resultant values of J fall within this narrow range of energy.

§ 6. HYDROGEN IONS

We saw above that in discussing the stability of singly charged ions, which on neutralisation will form neutral atoms, we must take into account any tendency of these neutral atoms to stick together. The formation of diatomic molecules on neutralisation is not confined to negative ions, but occurs also in the formation of H_2 molecules from positive hydrogen ions. When determining the conditions under which hydrogen ions will capture an electron from another species of particle in solution, we must follow a similar argument to that used for halogen ions. The normal energy of the vacant level of the hydrogen ion is $(\mathscr{I} - W)$. Suppose now that hydrogen ions are making encounters with a species of particle possessing an occupied electronic level rather *lower* than this—a level from which the electron would not normally be transferred. The energy liberated when two separate hydrogen ions are neutralised is $2(\mathscr{I} - W)$; but since the atoms tend to form a molecule H_2, the energy liberated for a pair of ions may be more; but it cannot be greater than $2(\mathscr{I} - W) + D$, where D is the dissociation energy of the H_2 molecule. For the hydrogen ion the quantity $(\mathscr{I} - W + \frac{1}{2}D)$ plays an important part, and in the next chapter we shall denote it by J'_H.

CHAPTER XV

§ 1. RESTRICTIONS ON THE SPECIES OF IONS

We have accumulated all the material to enable us to say under what conditions a species of ion can exist in solution. When we review the list of ions which are actually found, we must explain, not only why some species are not found at all, but also why some well-known species do not occur under particular circumstances. Under this second heading we have already seen that some species of ions will be incompatible with one another—some positive ions will capture electrons from certain species of negative ions, but not from others. Then again, the presence of a soluble electrode often introduces a restriction on the degrees of ionisation of its own ions. Although an insoluble electrode will, as we have seen, come into equilibrium with any mixed solution containing a metal in two stages of ionisation, this is not true of an electrode of the soluble metal itself. For most elements only one stage of ionisation can be in equilibrium with an electrode of the same metal—e.g. ferrous in contact with an iron electrode and not ferric ions in appreciable quantity, cupric ions in contact with copper and not cuprous.

We may begin this subject by asking what are the most highly charged ions which are known to occur. It seems to be generally assumed that aqueous solutions of ceric salts contain four times ionised cerium, Ce^{++++} ions. And the most natural explanation of Hevesy's experiment with plumbic salts, described in Chapter IX, is that the lead core becomes free in the form Pb^{++++}. There seems to be no evidence to show whether for any element ions bearing five charges exist in solution or not.

It is unnecessary to spend time discussing the absence of ions more highly charged than those which are found to occur for each element. We shall not expect to find ions of higher degree than Al^{+++}, Ca^{++}, Na^+ and so on. To remove a further electron involves breaking into a closed shell; and though the higher ionic charge would mean the usual increase in the solvation energy received, yet this increment would be insufficient to counterbalance the work done, which is exceptionally large in these cases, as seen in Table XI. It is only the missing ions of lower degree, like Fe^+ and Ca^+, that we need discuss. To do this we may begin by considering additional ways in which ions may disappear from solution.

In a vapour we always take it for granted that we shall not find some neutral atoms capturing electrons from their neighbours, spontaneously changing themselves into negative and positive ions according to the process

$$A + A \rightarrow A^- + A^+ \qquad \ldots\ldots(102).$$

When an atom A takes up an additional electron, to form A^-, the energy liberated is always less than the work required to ionise the same atom to A^+. The process indicated in (102) therefore requires work, and does not occur.

Similarly, in a vacuum we do not find positive ions of any element capturing electrons from their neighbours according to the process

$$A^+ + A^+ \rightarrow A^{++} + A \qquad \ldots\ldots(103).$$

The energy liberated when a singly charged ion captures an electron is always smaller than the work required to remove a second electron from the same, or from an identical ion, to form A^{++}. As pointed out in Chapter II, successive ionisation potentials *in vacuo* are for each element progressively larger. Consequently the reaction (103) will go from right to left, but not from left to right.

Turning now to ions in solution, we recall that for solvated ions the familiar progression in the ionisation potentials is often absent. The work to remove an electron from A^+ may actually be less than the energy liberated when A^+ captures an electron. In this case when one A^+ ion collides with another, the vacant level of either ion is lower than the occupied level of the other and an electron may be transferred. Clearly a solution containing only singly charged A^+ ions cannot exist. The reaction

(103) will go from left to right with liberation of energy, and the number of A^+ ions remaining in equilibrium with the A^{++} may be below the limit of detection.

We can go on now to show that for metallic ions the condition is even more stringent. Even if work is required to convert two A^+ ions into an A^{++} ion and a neutral A atom, this is not sufficient to ensure stability for a solution of A^+ ions. For when the neutral atoms are formed, they will stick together to form a particle of metal, liberating energy equal to the sublimation energy S. Consider then a metal A for which a definite amount of work to convert the two A^+ ions into A^{++} and a neutral atom A. Even then a solution containing only A^+ ions will not be stable, if this amount of work is small compared with S; the ions will change over spontaneously to the higher valency with deposition of metal, until an equilibrium is reached.

Although for simplicity we have discussed singly changing over to doubly charged ions, the argument is applicable to a change from any degree m to degree m'. The salts of gold and of indium in aqueous solution seem to afford examples of this behaviour. Thus indium dichloride forms colourless crystals; in water these do not go into solution as such, but are immediately decomposed into metallic indium and indium trichloride, which remains in solution:

$$3InCl_2 \rightarrow In + 2InCl_3 \qquad ......(104).$$

Indium dibromide deposits metallic indium in the same way. An aqueous solution of aurous chloride, AuCl, similarly deposits metallic gold, changing over to auric chloride, $AuCl_3$, until an equilibrium is reached.

§ 2. RESTRICTIONS IMPOSED BY THE SOLVENT

In the preceding section we found a restriction in ionic species due to a factor which did not depend directly on the properties of the particular solvent molecules among which the ions were dissolved. We shall find, however, that more important restrictions arise from the interaction between ions and solvent. In Chapter v we drew attention to the obvious fact that no ion could exist in a solvent if it possessed a vacant level lower than the levels occupied by the valence electrons of the solvent itself. Since then we have taken into account the fact that some solvents are themselves dissociated into ions—into negative ions, each possessing a supernumerary electron in a certain occupied level, and into positive ions, each having a vacancy for an electron in a certain level; from the fact that the solvent molecule dissociates into two ions, and not into two neutral particles, we know that the occupied level of the one is lower than the vacant level of the other. When dissolving any substance, the existence of these solvent ions must not be neglected. The electronic levels of the dissolved particles must be considered in relation to the vacant and occupied electronic levels of the solvent ions in a way similar to that which we followed among the solute ions themselves.

The argument can be set forth most clearly by choosing some particular solvent to discuss; for this we shall of course choose water, since for all other solvents the data are very incomplete; we shall have to discuss the electronic levels of the solute in relation to those of hydrogen and hydroxyl ions. Suppose we introduce into water a species of particle having an occupied electronic level higher than the vacant level of the $(H_3O)^+$ ion. It does not matter whether this solute particle is a neutral atom, a negative ion, or a positive ion; let us call the species A. When, on collision, an electron is transferred to a hydrogen ion, the neutralised H_3O will split up into a hydrogen atom and a water molecule. Pure water contains, as we have seen, between 10^{13} and 10^{14} hydrogen and hydroxyl ions per c.c. This number is maintained constant by the continual dissociation of H_2O molecules and the recombination of ions to form H_2O molecules—processes which go on independently of one another. If we introduce into water a large number of the particles A, most of the hydrogen ions are neutralised immediately, and the recombination to form H_2O is practically stopped. But the dissociation of the water molecules into ions goes on as before. The fresh crop of hydrogen ions produced by this continued dissociation will in their turn capture electrons from some of the remaining A particles, and so on, until the number of A particles remaining is too small to be detected.

We clearly have here a severe restriction upon the species of particles which can exist in aqueous solution; and we can at once go further. In the last paragraph we were supposing that the occupied electronic level of the A particle lay higher than the vacant level of $(H_3O)^+$. But, as we have seen at the end of the preceding chapter, $(H_3O)^+$ ions can capture electrons out of levels which are actually lower than the normal energy of their own vacant levels. This is because the H atoms have a tendency to form diatomic molecules similar to that of iodine atoms. In practice, however, the case of H_2 differs from that of iodine in several ways. In the first place, since the H_2 is a gas with a low solubility in water, unless it is prevented it tends to escape from the solution, however low its concentration. This escape is accompanied by a continual increase of entropy, which allows heat to flow into the solution from the surroundings and so to contribute towards the 0.59 ϵ-volt needed for the dissociation of the water molecules.

In the second place, in pure water the concentration of the hydrogen ions is much lower than could conveniently be used for iodine ions. And thirdly, the dissociation energy of H_2 being 4.48 ϵ-volts, the value of $\frac{1}{2}D$ which we have to introduce is as much as 2.24 ϵ-volts; that is to say, the gap between J_H and J_H' is more than 2 ϵ-volts. A particle having an occupied level whose energy falls in this gap will be unstable, but the position of the limit of stability is less clear-cut than in the case of iodine. According as the occupied level is high or low, the rate of transfer of electrons will be rapid or slow—perhaps too slow to be detected; the higher the occupied level, the more unstable will the particle be. The restriction due to the presence of hydrogen ions in water applies to both positive and negative ions. Whereas in a vacuum for most metallic elements the positive ions are known in various stages of ionisation, in aqueous solution some of these stages do not occur because the solvated ion possesses too high an occupied electronic level.

Turning next to the presence of hydroxyl ions in pure water, we see that the converse argument will apply. Any species of particle possessing a vacant electronic level lower than the occupied level of $(OH)^-$ will be unable to exist in aqueous solution. And we can again push the restriction somewhat further, since in exceptionally favourable collisions an electron can be transferred to a vacant level which is actually *higher* than the normal electronic level of $(OH)^-$, the neutralised OH being removed by the formation of H_2O_2 and O_2 molecules:

$$2OH \rightarrow H_2O_2 \rightarrow H_2O + \tfrac{1}{2}O_2 \qquad \ldots\ldots(105).$$

Just as for a halogen negative ion J'_- differs from J_- by the amount $\tfrac{1}{2}D$, so here for the hydroxyl ion we need to consider the appropriate J'_- which differs from its J_- by the maximum amount of energy that may be liberated per neutralised hydroxyl, i.e. one-half of the energy of the reaction (105).

The presence of hydroxyl ions in water imposes a severe restriction on particles in aqueous solution, although the position of the limit is even less clear-cut than in the case of the hydrogen ions. The lower the vacant level of the particle, the more rapidly will it capture electrons from the hydroxyl ions.

Combining this restriction with the previous one, we see that, to exist in aqueous solution, an ion must fulfil two conditions: its highest occupied electronic level must lie lower than the J' of the hydrogen ion, and its lowest vacant level must lie higher than the J'_- of the hydroxyl ion.

All the familiar ions in aqueous solution satisfy these two conditions, with a few exceptions which give metastable solutions.

In passing, we may notice that for non-aqueous solutions similar limitations must apply in every solvent which is self-dissociated into ions. Each solvent will impose its own limits, namely the values of J' and J'_- of the ions into which it dissociates. Unfortunately, the necessary data have not yet been collected, and we shall continue to discuss substances in aqueous solution. It was pointed out above that, when a solution is metastable, the evolution of H_2 or O_2 will be fast or slow according as the activation energy is small or large. These remarks were intended to refer to substances dissolved in pure water at room temperature, containing the ordinary number of hydrogen and hydroxyl ions. We know, however, that we can reduce the number of hydroxyl ions in water by any factor up to several million times; we do this by adding an acid to the water, when most of the hydroxyl ions in the water will combine with some of the added hydrogen ions to form H_2O molecules. When, therefore, we have a solute like that discussed above, which liberates oxygen from water by electron capture from hydroxyl ions, we may by the addition of an acid enormously reduce the rate of reaction, perhaps beyond the point where it is perceptible at room temperature.

Take, for example, the substance cobaltic sulphate. The green crystals $Co_2(SO_4)_3 . 18H_2O$ dissolve in water, furnishing the cobaltic ion Co^{+++}. The vacant level of this ion is so low that it captures an electron from $(OH)^-$ to form Co^{++}, and oxygen is evolved briskly at room temperature. The rate of liberation of oxygen is, however, much smaller if dilute sulphuric acid is added to the solution, and smaller still if the temperature is reduced.

At the other end of the scale, when we have a species of ion which is liberating hydrogen slowly by electron transfer, the situation is the converse of the above. Whatever be the rate of transfer in pure water, it will be *accelerated* by increasing the number of hydrogen ions, that is by the addition of an acid. For example, if we dissolve crystals of chromium disulphate or chromium dichloride in water, we obtain the doubly charged ion Cr^{++}. The occupied electronic level in this ion has an energy lying in the gap between J_H and J'_H; that is to say, the occupied level lies well below the normal vacant level of $(H_3O)^+$, but not by an amount sufficient to give a completely stable solution. By loss of an electron the ion changes into the chromic ion Cr^{+++}. The evolution of hydrogen is extremely slow at room temperature, but is accelerated by the addition of HCl.

In this slow evolution of gas each hydrogen molecule has been formed by a process which, as we have seen, is of rare occurrence, involving the neutralisation of two hydrogen ions, followed or accompanied by the formation of a H_2 molecule. In the solution this process only comes about through exceptionally favourable encounters. The reaction will be accelerated if we provide a surface where H atoms may be adsorbed, and may readily combine with their neighbours. Thus if a piece of platinum is placed in an aqueous solution containing the ion Cr^{++}, it is found that the change over to Cr^{+++} with evolution of hydrogen is much more rapid at the surface of the metal.

The conditions needed for retarding the evolution of hydrogen are the converse of those for the retardation of oxygen. The number of hydrogen ions in pure water may be enormously reduced by the addition of a solution containing hydroxyl ions, which will combine with most of the hydrogen ions, to form water molecules. The life of the Cr^{+++} ions cannot, however, be prolonged by these means. When we add a solution containing $(OH)^-$ ions, many of these, instead of combining with the $(H_3O)^+$ to form H_2O, combine with Cr to form $(CrOH)^+$ and $Cr(OH)_2$.

What has been said in these paragraphs of the chromous ion appears to be true also of the ion of vanadium V^{++}. In aqueous solution it changes over to V^{+++}, liberating hydrogen slowly. The occupied level of this ion seems to have an energy very near that of Cr^{++}.

§ 3. THE LIMITS IN AQUEOUS SOLUTION

We may pass on now to study the whole question quantitatively. A glance at Table VIII on page 175 shows us that the value of J'_H cannot be more than 4·5 ϵ-volts; otherwise, the familiar aqueous solutions of iodides would not exist; the iodine negative ions would rapidly lose their electrons. We shall, indeed, find that J'_H has a value smaller than this. By making use of the known heats of formation and solution of HCl, we can obtain the value of the heat of solvation of a hydrogen ion by means of a cycle. Taking equal numbers of hydrogen atoms and chlorine atoms in a vacuum, we can combine them and then allow the HCl molecules to dissolve in a large quantity of water, which they will do in the form of solvated ions. Alternatively, starting with the H and Cl atoms in a vacuum, we can transfer an electron from each H to Cl, and then plunge the H^+ and Cl^- ions into water; the final result will be the same as before. In this way we find that the heats of solvation of H^+ and Cl^- together amount to 14·9 ϵ-volts, which means that the heat of solvation of the H^+ ion is 12·1 ϵ-volts. We may take the value of the solvation energy to be 12·0 ϵ-volts. The value of $(\mathscr{I} - W)$ is thus $(13·53 - 12·0)$ ϵ-volts. Any species of particle having an occupied level at a depth of 2 ϵ-volts, or even more, would very rapidly lose its electron. Since the dissociation energy of the H_2 molecule is 4·48 ϵ-volts, the value of $(\mathscr{I} - W + \frac{1}{2}D)$ for the hydrogen ion is found to be $(13·53 - 12·0 + 2·24)$ or 3·8 ϵ-volts.

The behaviour of the ion Cr^{++} is clearly consistent with this value. In Table IX we found that the occupied electronic level of this ion lies at about 3·67 ϵ-volts. It is, therefore, a borderline case; the transfer of electrons is very slow except under favourable circumstances, such as at a surface where H_2 molecules can be formed easily.

Fig. 43 has already been referred to in the previous chapter. In this diagram the area above 3·8 ϵ-volts on the left-hand side has been shaded; this is the range of energy where occupied levels are impossible in aqueous solution. Similarly, the other shaded area on the right-hand side shows the beginning of the energies where vacant levels are impossible in aqueous solution. From its behaviour we know that the cobalt ion Co^{+++} is a borderline case; its vacant level lies certainly within the range of instability.

Fig. 43 enables us to understand more clearly several features to which attention has already been drawn. We can see in greater detail the origin of the limitation which was mentioned in connection with Table IX and which was summed up in the empirical rule—Of the metallic elements which exist in aqueous solution in two successive stages of ionisation the position of the electronic level concerned always lies in a narrow range of energy of which the upper and lower limits are roughly 3·6 ϵ-volts and 5·9 ϵ-volts. Take any stable pair of ions, like Fe^{++} and Fe^{+++}, and consider where their various electronic levels must fall in fig. 43. The occupied levels of both ions must fall below the upper shaded area. The vacant levels of both ions must fall above the lower shaded area. But we are now thoroughly familiar with the fact that the energy of the occupied level of Fe^{++} is identical with that of the vacant level of Fe^{+++}; both are, in fact, $_{2'}J_3$. The value of $_{2'}J_3$ for Fe must, therefore, lie between 3·6 and 5·9 ϵ-volts. The same argument applies to the value of $_{2'}J_3$ for the other metals, and to $_{3'}J_4$ for cerium, and so on; for an ion which exists in solution in any two successive stages of ionisation, m and $m+1$, the particular $_mJ_{m'}$ which connects these two degrees must lie in this central range of energy. The rule does not apply to any $_mJ_{m'}$ except this one. On the vacant level of Fe^{++} there is no restriction other than that common to all vacant

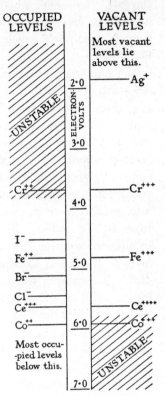

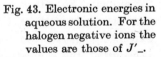

Fig. 43. Electronic energies in aqueous solution. For the halogen negative ions the values are those of J'_-.

levels. The vacant levels of most of the familiar ions lie well above this central range of energy. On the occupied level of Fe^{+++} there is no restriction except that common to all occupied levels. The occupied levels of both positive and negative ions lie in most cases below this central region. Consider, for example, the negative ions $(NO_3)^-$ and $(SO_4)^=$. As we have seen, an aqueous solution of cobaltic nitrate or sulphate is unstable, because the Co^{+++} ion tends to capture an electron from the hydroxyl ion; but it shows no signs of capturing an electron from the $(NO_3)^-$ ions or from the $(SO_4)^=$ ions, even when these are far more numerous than the hydroxyls. In each of these negative ions the occupied electronic level is apparently much deeper than the vacant level of the Co^{+++} ion.

In Chapter VIII, in introducing the ferric-ferrous half-cell, we drew attention to the way in which an electrode may be used to extract electrons from Fe^{++} ions, and, conversely, how Fe^{+++} ions may be steadily converted to Fe^{++} by the passage of a current. We asked to what extent this behaviour could be elicited among other species of ions—a question to which we can now give a detailed answer; we can prescribe the conditions which must be present in order that we may induce an ion to take up an electron, or alternatively may extract an electron from it. To reduce the charge on any species of ion A^{++} in aqueous solution, we must cause electrons from the critical level of the metal to escape to these A^{++} ions without at the same time causing them to escape to the $(H_3O)^+$ ions present in the solution. But if the depth of the vacant level of the A^{++} ion is less than J'_H, this will be impossible. For if we try to bring the vacant level of A^{++} below the critical level of the electrode, as in fig. 25 b, before this condition is reached electrons will already be escaping from the electrode to the $(H_3O)^+$ ions. It is for this reason that this electrode method cannot be used for reducing Fe^{++} to Fe^+, nor Al^{+++} to Al^{++}, nor Ca^{++} to Ca^+.

If we look next at the converse process, we see that in extracting an electron from a species of ion, we must do so without at the same time causing electrons from the $(OH)^-$ ions to escape to the electrode. In the case of the Co^{++} ion we can only do this with partial success; and for a species of ion whose occupied level is still lower it will be impossible.

CHAPTER XVI

§ 1. THE ELECTROCHEMICAL SERIES

It has long been known that the metals can be arranged in a series, such that each member in the list will displace from solution any metal occurring below it in the list. As usual, there are two methods by which this displacement may be carried out—by direct mixing, and indirectly by the use of a pair of electrodes. If, for example, zinc dust is shaken up in a solution of copper sulphate, the zinc goes into solution and an equivalent amount of copper is deposited. The free electrons which belonged to the metallic zinc will have been handed over to the copper. Alternatively, in the Daniell cell the zinc goes into solution in one vessel, and electrons, flowing thence along the wire in the external circuit, settle down in the copper, which is growing by deposition in the other half-cell.

As usual, we may measure the reverse e.m.f. which, inserted in the external circuit, just prevents this spontaneous current from flowing. The results of such experiments may be expressed by ascribing electrode potentials to standard half-cells in the way described before; that is, by allotting to each half-cell an arbitrary number such that the difference between any two of these numbers gives in volts the value of the e.m.f. of the corresponding cell. Table X gives a list of such electrode potentials for the metals in three different solvents, the value being in each case for the metal dipping into a solution containing its own ions at *unit activity*—a term which was explained in Chapter VII. The first column of figures gives the values in aqueous solution referred to the usual hydrogen electrode; the next column gives the values in methyl alcohol referred to the standard hydrogen electrode in methyl alcohol; and the last column gives the values in liquid ammonia referred to the standard hydrogen electrode in liquid ammonia. The values for the alkalis have been obtained from measurements using amalgams containing known quantities of the alkali metal; by a simple extrapolation one can calculate what would be the

TABLE X

STANDARD ELECTRODE POTENTIALS OF THE METALS IN WATER,* METHYL ALCOHOL,† AND LIQUID AMMONIA‡ RELATIVE TO HYDROGEN ELECTRODES

	Water	Methyl alcohol	Liquid NH_3 at $-50°$ C.
Li	-2.959_5	—	—
Rb	-2.925_9	—	—
K	-2.924_1	—	-1.98
Ca	-2.76	—	—
Na	-2.714_6	-2.728	-1.84
Zn	-0.761_8	—	-0.52
Fe	-0.441	—	—
Cd	-0.401_3	-0.258	-0.18
Tl	-0.336_0	-0.379	—
Ni	-0.231	—	—
Sn	-0.136	—	—
Pb	-0.122	—	$+0.33$
H	0.0	0.0	0.0
Cu	$+0.344_1$	$+0.490$	$+0.43$
Ag	$+0.797_8$	$+0.764$	$+0.83$
Hg	$+0.798_8$	—	$+0.75$
Au	$+1.36$	—	—

value for an electrode of the pure alkali metal itself; the fact that in practice only amalgams are used need not prevent us from discussing these values.

§ 2. THE BEHAVIOUR OF A BIMETALLIC CELL

We have seen in Chapter x that in any simple bimetallic cell the e.m.f. is the sum of three electrical double-layers. Of these three the double layer at the metal-metal contact in the external circuit turns out to be the most important, as first emphasised by Langmuir§ in 1916. Before discussing the electrodes of a

* Int. Crit. Tables.
† Buckley and Hartley, *Phil. Mag.* **8**, 320 (1929).
‡ Pleskov and Monossohn, *Acta Physicochimica, U.S.S.R.* **2**, 621 (1935).
§ Langmuir, *Trans. Amer. Electrochem. Soc.* **29**, 125 (1916); Butler, *Phil. Mag.* **48**, 927 (1924).

bimetallic cell, let us first consider pieces of any two metals, A and B, put into electrical connection through a third piece of metal M, fig. 44 a. When contact is made between A and M, their electrons at once become levelled up, as in fig. 14 c; and in the same way, when contact is made between B and M, their electrons are levelled up too. It follows then, that if we fix attention now on the metals A and B, we shall find that their electrons are already levelled up, as if they were in direct contact with each other. By putting both A and B into contact with the metal M, we have already brought the tops of their electron distributions to the same level.

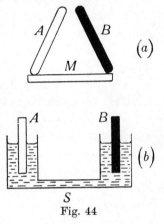

(a)

(b)

Fig. 44

If now the free end of the metal A, fig. 44 a, is made to touch the free end of B, no passage of electrons across the new junction will take place—or rather, the movement of the free electrons will be equal in the two directions. Electrical double layers exist at the junctions A–M and B–M, and the sum of the strengths of these two double layers has of necessity the value which exactly levels up the electrons in A and B.

With this example let us now contrast the situation of the metal electrodes A and B of any simple bimetallic cell, fig. 44 b. These electrodes are in electrical connection with each other, not through any metallic conductor, but through the conducting solutions S. At the interface between the metal A and the liquid S there may be an electrical double layer, and there may be another double layer between S and B. If the strengths of these double layers are called V_A and V_B, there is no reason why the sum $V_A + V_B$ should have the value which levels up the electrons in the metals; in general it does not. Consequently, when the free ends of A and B are put into contact, electrons stream from A to B, or vice versa. The first essential property of the electrolyte in any bimetallic cell is that it enables us to put two different metals into electrical connection with each other without levelling up the free electrons in them. Secondly, when, on contact, electrons are transferred from one metal to the other, the electrolyte prevents this flow of electrons from being a merely transient effect.

Since the work function of any piece of metal is independent of the size of the piece, the value of the contact p.d. between any two pieces of metal will be independent of their sizes. If, when contact is made between the two terminals of a bimetallic cell, electrons are transferred from A to B, the positive charge which grows on A immediately causes positive cores of the metal A to go into solution. The result is merely that the size of the piece of metal A has been diminished; it is still electrically neutral, the positive cores having left by one route, and the electrons by another. Simultaneously the size of the piece of metal B has been increased by deposition of ions of B, and by receiving the electrons from A. The electrical condition of each piece of metal is, therefore, the same as before. We see that as far as the metal-metal contact is concerned the situation is unchanged, since the strength of the electronic double layer is independent of the sizes of the pieces of metal involved. The transfer of electrons across the junction, instead of tending to bring about the deadlock of fig. 14 c, has done nothing to level up the electrons. The flow of electrons accordingly continues.

The part played by the metal-metal contact can best be illustrated by considering what happens when we couple together two particular half-cells. As one of these half-cells we may take the silver electrode which has already been mentioned in Chapter XIV. We saw there that for Ag^+ in aqueous solution the value of W is about 0·2 ϵ-volt greater than the value of Y; and that, consequently, when a silver electrode is dipping into a solution containing its own ions at moderate concentration an electrical double layer of strength 0·1 ϵ-volt, or less, will suffice to bring about equilibrium at the interface. The electronic work function ϕ of metallic silver is said to be 4·74 ϵ-volts.

As soon as accurate values of ϕ are available for a greater number of metals it will be possible to give a more detailed discussion of this subject. For the alkali metals different workers agree in finding values of ϕ in the neighbourhood of 2·0 ϵ-volts. The strength of the electronic double layer at the contact between a silver electrode and an electrode of an alkali metal would accordingly amount to about 2·7 ϵ-volts. That is to say, the electrode potential to be allotted to the alkali metal in Table X would be as much as 2·7 ϵ-volts negative with respect to the silver electrode in virtue of the metal-metal contact alone. Actually, as will be seen from Table X, the values allotted to Na both in aqueous and methyl alcohol solutions are more than 3·4 ϵ-volts negative with respect to silver. This is due to the fact that in both these solvents the solvation energy of the Na$^+$ ion is greater than Y, so that $(W - Y)$ is a positive quantity and makes a contribution to the e.m.f. which is *added* to the metal contact potential difference. On the other hand, in liquid ammonia the electrode potential allotted to Na is 2·8 ϵ-volts negative with respect to Ag, which is little more than the difference in the electronic work-functions of the two metals.

§ 3. ENERGY AND E.M.F.

The traditional idea of the working of a bimetallic cell is very different from the description which has just been given. According to the theory tentatively put forward by Nernst in 1889, when any noble metal, that is any metal near the bottom of Table X, is dipped into a solution containing its own ions at moderate concentration, some ions are deposited on the metal, setting up a double layer positive outwards. This behaviour was said to be in direct contrast to that of any base metal near the top of the series, which throws ions into solution and acquires a double layer positive outwards. The electrochemical series of the metals was supposed to arise from these contrasted modes of behaviour, the e.m.f. of any simple bimetallic cell being just the algebraic sum of these double layers at the metal-solution interface in each half-cell. In many text-books the electrode potential of a metal is regarded as being a measure of the "difference of potential between a metal and a solution containing its own ions".

On the other hand, as we have seen, the electrochemical series of the metals seems to be a matter of their characteristic electronic work functions, the elements in the lower half of Table X being those with large values of ϕ, and those near the top of the series having a small value of ϕ. When coupled together, the former provides the positive, and the latter the negative terminal of the cell. When the external circuit of a bimetallic cell is closed, free electrons from the baser metal tend to spill over into the vacant electronic levels of the nobler metal which has a larger ϕ, as illustrated in fig. 14 a. This is often helped by the additional contribution from the interfaces inside the cell. But if in any cell this contribution were zero there might still be a large e.m.f. arising from the strength of the double layer at the metal-metal contact alone.

When a cell is generating a current, however small, energy is being used up at a definite rate. If, for example, the current flowing is exactly 10^{-7} ampere, and energy is being expended at the rate of $\mathscr{E}$ ergs per second, the value of the e.m.f. of the cell in volts is just $\mathscr{E}$. Or, in other words, if $\mathscr{E}$ ergs are available for the transfer of 10^{-7} coulomb, the e.m.f. of the cell is $\mathscr{E}$ volts, one watt being equal to 10^7 ergs per second. According to this view the characteristic e.m.f. of a cell is determined by the amount of energy available per unit charge transferred, the dimensions of an e.m.f. being "energy divided by electric charge". The energy is, of course, derived from the chemical reaction taking place inside the cell, the replacement of one metal in solution by another—in the Daniell cell the replacement of copper by zinc—a reaction which may be performed directly by shaking up finely divided metal in a solution containing ions of the other metal. In this case the energy is converted into heat:

$$Cu^{++} + Zn_{metal} \rightarrow Cu_{metal} + Zn^{++} + 50,110 \text{ calories}$$
$$\ldots\ldots(106).$$

It is well known that if the 50,110 calories is divided by the total charge transferred, namely two faradays, the result is 1·09 volts, which is equal to the e.m.f. $\mathscr{E}$ of the cell. In a cell whose e.m.f. varies with temperature, the heat evolved in the equivalent reaction at temperature T is given by the Gibbs-Helmholtz expression $\mathscr{E} - Td\mathscr{E}/dT$.

In any cell the metal-metal contact in the external circuit seems to have no connection with processes taking place inside the cell, and to be incapable of supplying energy for driving the current. This gave rise to the idea that the strength of the double layer at this contact could form no appreciable part of the total e.m.f. Yet we have seen that it often forms the major part of the e.m.f. and must then furnish the major part of the heat of reaction. In a particular cell it might even furnish the whole of the e.m.f. and the whole heat of reaction. To show that there is really no objection to this conclusion, we may consider once more the energy liberated when an ion goes into solution from a metal surface. In fig. 27 we saw that in the absence of an electrical double layer at the interface this is equal to $(W - Y)$; and in the presence of a layer of strength V it is equal to $(W - Y + n\epsilon V)$ or $(Z + n\epsilon V)$. When ions are deposited, the energy liberated per ion is the same with opposite sign.

Suppose then that at a zinc surface where zinc cores are going into solution there exists a double layer having any arbitrary strength which we may call V_{Zn}, and that at a copper surface where Cu^{++} cores are being deposited there is a layer of strength V_{Cu}. If one Cu core is deposited and one Zn core goes into solution, the energy liberated is clearly

$$(Z_{Zn} + 2\epsilon V_{Zn}) - (Z_{Cu} + 2\epsilon V_{Cu}) = 2\epsilon \ (V_{Zn} - V_{Cu}) - (Z_{Cu} - Z_{Zn})$$
$$\ldots\ldots(107).$$

Suppose now that the reaction is taking place by direct mixing, and that fig. 45 represents a particular grain of zinc with a film of copper on its side; the zinc is steadily dissolving and the copper film is growing by deposition. Let S be any point in the solution near the edge of the copper film, C any point in the film and Z any neighbouring point in the zinc. The difference of electrical potential between the points Z and C is, of course, equal to the p.d. between Z and S *minus* the p.d. between C and S. Since both metal and solution are conductors, any p.d. between Z and S is equal to the strength of the surface double layer which we have called V_{Zn}, and any p.d. between C and S is equal to V_{Cu}. Hence the p.d. between Z and C is equal to $(V_{Zn} - V_{Cu})$.

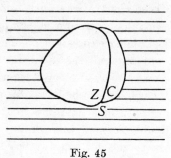

Fig. 45

If we consider the potential energy of an electron along the line ZC through the two metals, we see that it is given by a curve like fig. 14 c; the strength of the electronic double layer at the junction of the metals is equal to $(\phi_{Cu} - \phi_{Zn})$. The potential difference between the points Z and C is equal to the strength of this double layer; we may, therefore, substitute for $(V_{Zn} - V_{Cu})$ in (107) and obtain for the energy liberated the value

$$2\epsilon \, (\phi_{Cu} - \phi_{Zn}) - (Z_{Cu} - Z_{Zn}) \qquad ......(108).$$

This is the value per divalent ion; the energy per electronic charge transferred will be half of this. For any pair of metals whose ionic valencies are n_A and n_B, the heat of reaction per electronic charge will be

$$(\phi_A - \phi_B) - \left(\frac{Z_A}{n_A} - \frac{Z_B}{n_B}\right) \qquad ......(109).$$

The quantity $(Y - W)$ which we have been using applies to the lowest level of the ions, and we have been neglecting the effect of any difference between the thermal energy of one species of ions and the other. But, as kT is only $0 \cdot 025$ ϵ-volt at room temperature, this does not affect the argument. Since the second term in (109) is often small compared with the first, we see that there is certainly no objection to the idea that the metal-metal contact in the external circuit of a cell may provide the major part, or even the whole, of the e.m.f. of the cell.

An objection of a different kind has sometimes been urged against this point of view. It is pointed out that in the experimental measurement of ϕ for a metal it is difficult to get reproducible results owing to the presence of adsorbed films; and it is argued that the whole metal-metal contact potential must be unimportant, otherwise wide fluctuations in the e.m.f.s of cells would result. This objection rests on a complete misunderstanding. To measure the e.m.f. of a cell, we close the external circuit by means of a potentiometer wire. At each junction the top of the electron distribution in the interior of one metal becomes levelled up with that in the other, as in fig. 14 c; and it makes not the slightest difference to the resultant double layer whether impurity atoms are present at the junction or not.

The same is true when a metal is in contact with a solution. Take for example a platinum electrode dipping into a standard ferric-ferrous solution. In order that there may be equilibrium there must be a double layer of strength $(J - \phi)$, where ϕ is the characteristic work function of *clean* platinum. If, to take an extreme case, due to adsorbed atoms there were on the surface of the platinum already an electrical double layer which happened by chance to have just this required strength, then on dipping the metal into the solution there would be equilibrium without the customary transference of charge which usually sets up the necessary double layer. If, on the other hand, the sign of the initial double layer on the platinum is the opposite of that required, then on dipping the metal into the solution an abnormally large transference of charge takes place until again the strength of the layer reaches the required value $(J - \phi)$. The values of the work functions with which we deal are always those characteristic of clean metals. The same is true if a preferential orientation of solvent molecules against the electrode surface gives rise to a double layer; the necessary strength of the total double layer is unchanged.

We shall conclude this chapter by considering one more problem in the same field. In Chapter x, in discussing a cell containing an insoluble electrode in each half-cell, we took the two electrodes to be of the same metal. But this need not be so; one electrode may be of platinum, with $\phi = 6\cdot3$ ϵ-volts, while the second electrode is of some other insoluble metal with its own characteristic work function. Even if dissimilar electrodes are never used in practice, it is important that the properties of such a cell should be understood in detail. For we saw in expression (50) that, in a half-cell of this kind, the strength V of the electrical double layer at the metal-solution interface depends on the value of ϕ of the electrode. Suppose first that two electrodes of different metals are dipping into identical mixed solutions, containing a certain metallic ion in two stages of ionisation. The value of ϕ in one half-cell will be different from that in the other. On the metal with the smaller ϕ the double layer will be more positive inwards. This difference in the strengths of the double layers would give rise to an e.m.f. of the magnitude

$$\epsilon \, (V_A - V_B) = -(\phi_A - \phi_B) \qquad \ldots\ldots(110),$$

were it not for the fact that in the external circuit there is a metal contact p.d. which has the equal and opposite value $(\phi_A - \phi_B)$. The three double layers exactly cancel each other out, and the e.m.f. of this cell is zero, as indeed it must be if the mixed solutions are identical, since there is no energy nor change of entropy to drive the current.

We may pass on next to a cell where not only the insoluble electrodes are different, but also the species of ions; let each half-cell contain a standard mixed solution, the ionisation potentials being J_A and J_B, as in (50). The strength of the double layer V_A now differs from V_B by the amount

$$\epsilon \, (V_A - V_B) = (J_A - J_B) - (\phi_A - \phi_B) \qquad \ldots\ldots(111).$$

But when we come to consider the whole e.m.f. of the cell, the second term is exactly cancelled by the third double layer in the external circuit, leaving a total e.m.f. equal to $J_A - J_B$, as in (51). In the list of experimental oxidation-reduction potentials given in Table IV it was not stated what metal was used as the electrode; nor was there any need to do so; when any of these half-cells is coupled to a standard half-cell, the e.m.f. of the cell will not depend on what metal is being used as the insoluble electrode, although the component double layers will be different.

TABLE XI
SUCCESSIVE IONISATION POTENTIALS *IN VACUO* (COMPARE FIG. 5)
Electron-volts

1	H	—	13·53	—	—	—
2	He	—	24·47	54·14	—	—
3	Li	—	5·36	75·26	121·84	—
4	Be	—	9·28	18·12	153·11	216·63
5	B	—	8·25	25·00	37·74	258·03
6	C	—	11·20	24·26	47·64	64·17
7	N	—	14·46	29·44	47·20	72·04
8	O	—	13·55	34·94	54·63	77·03
9	F	4·1	18·6	34·81	62·35	86·72
10	Ne	—	21·47	40·91	63·3	(97)
11	Na	—	5·11	47·07	71·31	98·41
12	Mg	—	7·61	14·96	79·74	108·77
13	Al	—	5·96	18·73	28·31	119·39
14	Si	—	8·08	16·26	33·33	44·92
15	P	—	11·11	19·80	30·02	51·1
16	S	—	10·31	23·29	34·88	47·08
17	Cl	3·8	12·96	23·10	39·71	53·20
18	Ar	—	15·69	27·72	40·72	—
19	K	—	4·32	31·7	48·37	(62·5)
20	Ca	—	6·09	11·82	50·9	69·9
21	Sc	—	6·7	12·8	24·63	74·3
22	Ti	—	6·81	13·6	27·6	43·06
23	V	—	6·76	14·1	26·4	(48)
24	Cr	—	6·74	16·6	(27)	(50)
25	Mn	—	7·39	15·70	(32)	(52)
26	Fe	—	7·83	16·16	—	—
27	Co	—	8·5	17·3	—	—
28	Ni	—	7·61	18·2	—	—
29	Cu	—	7·68	20·2	29·5	—
30	Zn	—	9·36	17·89	39·5	—
31	Ga	—	5·97	20·43	30·6	63·8
32	Ge	—	8·09	15·9	34·1	45·5
33	As	—	10·5	20·1	28·19	49·9
34	Se	—	9·70	—	—	—
35	Br	3·6	11·30	—	(26)	50·0
36	Kr	—	13·94	24·47	36·8	—
37	Rb	—	4·16	27·3	—	—
38	Sr	—	5·67	10·98	(42·8)	—
39	Y	—	6·5	12·3	20·4	—
40	Zr	—	6·92	13·97	24·00	33·8
47	Ag	—	7·54	21·9	29·25	—
48	Cd	—	8·96	16·84	38·0	—
49	In	—	5·76	18·81	27·91	57·8
50	Sn	—	7·30	14·52	30·49	40·5
51	Sb	—	8·35	(18)	—	—
52	Te	—	8·96	—	29·5	—
53	I	3·2*	10·44	—	—	—
54	X	—	12·08	(24)	—	—
55	Cs	—	3·87	23·4	—	—
56	Ba	—	5·19	9·95	(35·5)	—

* Mayer and Helmholtz, *Zeit. f. Phys.* **75**, 29 (1932); Sutton and Mayer, *J. Chem. Phys.* **3**, 20 (1935).

TABLE XII

IONIC CRYSTALS

	Lattice energy at $0°$ K.* kcal.	Thermal energy at $291°$ K. kcal.	Heat of solution at $291°$ K. kcal.	$(W + W_-)$ in H_2O at $291°$ K. kcal.	ϵ-volts
NaF	213·$_4$	1·9	−0·6	210·$_9$	9·1
NaCl	183·$_1$	2·4	−1·3	179·$_4$	7·8
NaBr	174·$_6$	2·5	−0·2	171·$_9$	7·5
NaI	163·$_9$	2·8	+1·4	162·$_5$	7·0
KF	189·$_7$	2·2	+4·1	191·$_6$	8·3
KCl	165·$_4$	2·5	−4·4	158·$_5$	6·9
KBr	159·$_3$	2·7	−5·1	151·$_5$	6·6
KI	150·$_8$	2·8	−5·1	142·$_9$	6·2

TABLE XIII

HEAT OF SOLVATION IN WATER AT $18°$ C. IN ELECTRON-VOLTS

F^-	4·2	K^+	4·1	Be^{++}	26·4	Ni^{++}	22·4
Cl^-	2·8	Rb^+	3·8	Mg^{++}	21·2	Cu^{++}	23·3
Br^-	2·5	Cs^+	3·5	Ca^{++}	17·7	Zn^{++}	22·9
I^-	2·1	Ag^+	5·5	Sr^{++}	16·6	Cd^{++}	20·1
Li^+	6·1	Tl^+	4·7	Ba^{++}	15·0	Hg^{++}	20·8
Na^+	5·0	H^+	12·1	Fe^{++}	21·7	Al^{+++}	50·0
				Co^{++}	22·6	In^{+++}	42·5

TABLE XIV

ENERGIES OF METALS IN ELECTRON-VOLTS

	Sublimation energy†	Electronic work function‡	Y_1
Cs	0·84	1·9	2·7
Rb	0·87	2·1	2·9
K	0·94	2·2	3·0
Ag	2·9	4·7	5·7
			Y_2
Co	3·7	4·1	21·3
Pt	5·44	6·3	—

* Born, Mayer and Helmholtz, *loc. cit.*
† Sherman, *Chem. Rev.* 11, 93 (1932).
‡ *Physical Rev.* vols. 32, 38, 41 and 45.

Table XV

Constants and Conversion Factors

Electronic charge	$\epsilon = 4\cdot77 \times 10^{-10}$ e.s.u.
Planck's constant	$h = 6\cdot55 \times 10^{-27}$ erg sec.
Boltzmann's constant	$k = 1\cdot37 \times 10^{-16}$ erg
Avogadro's number	$= 6\cdot06 \times 10^{23}$
Number of electrons in one coulomb	$= 6\cdot3 \times 10^{18}$
One electron-volt	$= 1\cdot59 \times 10^{-12}$ erg
One electron-volt per molecule	$= 23,050$ cals. per mol.

REFERENCES

For Chapters I–III:

  JEANS, *Electricity and Magnetism*, Chapters VI–VIII.

  DEBYE, *Polar Molecules*.

  GURNEY, *Elementary Quantum Mechanics*.

  BRAGG, *The Crystalline State*, vol. I, Chapter VII.

  MOTT and JONES, *The Properties of Metals and Alloys*.

  DE BOER, *Electron Emission and Adsorption Phenomena*.

For Chapters IV–XVI:

  DOLE, *Theoretical and Experimental Electrochemistry*.

  GLASSTONE, *The Electrochemistry of Solutions*.

  FALKENHAGEN, *Electrolytes*.

INDEX

CATALOGUE OF DOVER BOOKS

BOOKS EXPLAINING SCIENCE AND MATHEMATICS

Engineering, technology, applied science etc.

TEACH YOURSELF ELECTRICITY, C. W. Wilman. Electrical resistance, inductance, capacitance, magnets, chemical effects of current, alternating currents, generators and motors, transformers, rectifiers, much more. 230 questions, answers, worked examples. List of units. 115 illus. 194pp. 6⅞ x 4¼. Clothbound **$2.00**

ELEMENTARY METALLURGY AND METALLOGRAPHY, A. M. Shrager. Basic theory and descriptions of most of the fundamental manufacturing processes involved in metallurgy. Partial contents: the structure of metals; slip, plastic deformation, and recrystalization; iron ore and production of pig iron; chemistry involved in the metallurgy of iron and steel; basic processes such as the Bessemer treatment, open-hearth process, the electric arc furnace —with advantages and disadvantages of each; annealing, hardening, and tempering steel; copper, aluminum, magnesium, and their alloys. For freshman engineers, advanced students in technical high schools, etc. Index. Bibliography. 177 diagrams. 17 tables. 284 questions and problems. 27-page glossary. ix + 389pp. 5⅜ x 8. S138 Paperbound **$2.25**

BASIC ELECTRICITY, Prepared by the Bureau of Naval Personnel. Originally a training course text for U.S. Navy personnel, this book provides thorough coverage of the basic theory of electricity and its applications. Best book of its kind for either broad or more limited studies of electrical fundamentals . . . for classroom use or home study. Part 1 provides a more limited coverage of theory: fundamental concepts, batteries, the simple circuit, D.C. series and parallel circuits, conductors and wiring techniques, A.C. electricity, inductance and capacitance, etc. Part 2 applies theory to the structure of electrical machines—generators, motors, transformers, magnetic amplifiers. Also deals with more complicated instruments, synchros, servo-mechanisms. The concluding chapters cover electrical drawings and blueprints, wiring diagrams, technical manuals, and safety education. The book contains numerous questions for the student, with answers. Index and six appendices. 345 illustrations. x + 448pp. 6½ x 9¼. S973 Paperbound **$2.95**

BASIC ELECTRONICS, prepared by the U.S. Navy Training Publications Center. A thorough and comprehensive manual on the fundamentals of electronics. Written clearly, it is equally useful for self-study or course work for those with a knowledge of the principles of basic electricity. Partial contents: Operating Principles of the Electron Tube; Introduction to Transistors; Power Supplies for Electronic Equipment; Tuned Circuits; Electron-Tube Amplifiers; Audio Power Amplifiers; Oscillators; Transmitters; Transmission Lines; Antennas and Propagation; Introduction to Computers; and related topics. Appendix. Index. Hundreds of illustrations and diagrams. vi + 471pp. 6½ x 9¼. S1076 Paperbound **$2.75**

BASIC THEORY AND APPLICATION OF TRANSISTORS, Prepared by the U.S. Department of the Army. An introductory manual prepared for an army training program. One of the finest available surveys of theory and application of transistor design and operation. Minimal knowledge of physics and theory of electron tubes required. Suitable for textbook use, course supplement, or home study. Chapters: Introduction; fundamental theory of transistors; transistor amplifier fundamentals; parameters, equivalent circuits, and characteristic curves; bias stabilization; transistor analysis and comparison using characteristic curves and charts; audio amplifiers; tuned amplifiers; wide-band amplifiers; oscillators; pulse and switching circuits; modulation, mixing, and demodulation; and additional semiconductor devices. Unabridged, corrected edition. 240 schematic drawings, photographs, wiring diagrams, etc. 2 Appendices. Glossary. Index. 263pp. 6½ x 9¼. S380 Paperbound **$1.25**

TEACH YOURSELF HEAT ENGINES, E. De Ville. Measurement of heat, development of steam and internal combustion engines, efficiency of an engine, compression-ignition engines, production of steam, the ideal engine, much more. 318 exercises, answers, worked examples. Tables. 76 illus. 220pp. 6⅞ x 4¼. Clothbound **$2.00**

BOOKS EXPLAINING SCIENCE AND MATHEMATICS

Miscellaneous

ON THE SENSATIONS OF TONE, Hermann Helmholtz. This is an unmatched coordination of such fields as acoustical physics, physiology, experiment, history of music. It covers the entire gamut of musical tone. Partial contents: relation of musical science to acoustics, physical vs. physiological acoustics, composition of vibration, resonance, analysis of tones by sympathetic resonance, beats, chords, tonality, consonant chords, discords, progression of parts, etc. 33 appendixes discuss various aspects of sound, physics, acoustics, music, etc. Translated by A. J. Ellis. New introduction by Prof. Henry Margenau of Yale. 68 figures. 43 musical passages analyzed. Over 100 tables. Index. xix + 576pp. 6⅛ x 9¼. S114 Paperbound **$3.00**

THE NATURE OF LIGHT AND COLOUR IN THE OPEN AIR, M. Minnaert. Why is falling snow sometimes black? What causes mirages, the fata morgana, multiple suns and moons in the sky? How are shadows formed? Prof. Minnaert of the University of Utrecht answers these and similar questions in optics, light, colour, for non-specialists. Particularly valuable to nature, science students, painters, photographers. Translated by H. M. Kremer-Priest, K. Jay. 202 illustrations, including 42 photos. xvi + 362pp. 5⅜ x 8.   T196 Paperbound **$2.00**

THE PHYSICS OF MUSIC, Alexander Wood. Introduction for musicians to the physical aspect of sound. No scientific training necessary to understand concepts, etc. Wealth of material on origin and development of instruments, physical principles involved in the production of their sounds, pitch, intensity and loudness, mechanism of the ear, dissonance and consonance, sound reproduction and recordings, concert halls, etc. Extensively revised by Dr. J. M. Bowsher. Indices. Bibliography. 16 plates. 114 illustrations. 270pp. 5⅛ x 8⅛.
T322 Paperbound **$2.25**

GREAT IDEAS AND THEORIES OF MODERN COSMOLOGY, Jagjit Singh. The theories of Jeans, Eddington, Milne, Kant, Bondi, Gold, Newton, Einstein, Gamow, Hoyle, Dirac, Kuiper, Hubble, Weizsäcker and many others on such cosmological questions as the origin of the universe, space and time, planet formation, "continuous creation," the birth, life, and death of the stars, the origin of the galaxies, etc. By the author of the popular "Great Ideas of Modern Mathematics." A gifted popularizer of science, he makes the most difficult abstractions crystal-clear even to the most non-mathematical reader. Index. xii + 276 pp. 5⅜ x 8½.
T925 Paperbound **$1.85**

PIONEERS OF SCIENCE, O. Lodge. Eminent scientist-expositor's authoritative, yet elementary survey of great scientific theories. Concentrating on individuals—Copernicus, Brahe, Kepler, Galileo, Descartes, Newton, Laplace, Herschel, Lord Kelvin, and other scientists—the author presents their discoveries in historical order adding biographical material on each man and full, specific explanations of their achievements. The clear and complete treatment of the post-Newtonian astronomers is a feature seldom found in other books on the subject. Index. 120 illustrations. xv + 404pp. 5⅜ x 8.   T716 Paperbound **$1.65**

BIOGRAPHY OF SCIENTISTS

ISAAC NEWTON: A BIOGRAPHY, Louis Trenchard More. The definitive biography of Newton, his life and work. Presents Newton as a living man, with a critical, objective analysis of his character as well as a careful survey of his manifold accomplishments, scientific, theological, etc. The author, himself a professor of physics, has made full use of all of Newton's published works and all material in the Portsmouth Collection of Newton's personal and unpublished papers. The text includes numerous letters by Newton and his acquaintances, and many other of his papers—some translated from Latin to English by the author. A universally-esteemed work. Unabridged republication. 1 full-page plate. Index. xiii + 675pp. 5⅜ x 8½.
T579 Paperbound **$2.50**

PIERRE CURIE, Marie Curie. Mme. Curie, Nobel Prize winner, creates a memorable portrait of her equally famous husband and his lifelong scientific researches. She brings to life the determined personality of a great scientist at work. Her own autobiographical notes, included in this volume, reconstruct her own work on radiation which resulted in the isolation of radium. "A delightful book. It marks one of the few instances in which the proverbially humdrum life of the student of physical science, together with the austere ideals, has been made intelligible," New York Times. Unabridged reprint. Translated by Charlotte and Vernon Kellogg. Introduction by Mrs. Wm. Brown Meloney. 8 halftones. viii + 120pp. 5⅜ x 8½.
T199 Paperbound **$1.00**

THE BOOK OF MY LIFE (DE VITA PROPRIA LIBER), Jerome Cardan. The remarkable autobiography of an important Renaissance mathematician, physician, and scientist, who at the same time was a paranoid, morbid, superstitious man, consumed with ambition and self-love (and self-pity). These chronicles of his fortunes and misfortunes make absorbing reading, giving us an extremely insightful view of a man's reactions and sensations—the first psychological autobiography. Through his eyes we can also see the superstitions and beliefs of an age, Renaissance medical practices, and the problems that concerned a trained mind in the 16th century. Unabridged republication of original English edition, translated by Jean Stoner. Introduction. Notes. Bibliography. xviii + 331pp. 5⅜ x 8½.   T345 Paperbound **$1.60**

THE AUTOBIOGRAPHY OF CHARLES DARWIN, AND SELECTED LETTERS, edited by Francis Darwin. Darwin's own record of his early life; the historic voyage aboard the "Beagle"; the furor surrounding evolution, and his replies; reminiscences of his son. Letters to Henslow, Lyell, Hooker, Huxley, Wallace, Kingsley, etc., and thoughts on religion and vivisection. We see how he revolutionized geology with his concept of ocean subsidence; how his great books on variation of plants and animals, primitive man, the expression of emotion among primates, plant fertilization, carnivorous plants, protective coloration, etc., came into being. Appendix. Index. 365pp. 5⅜ x 8.   T479 Paperbound **$1.65**

PHILOSOPHY OF SCIENCE AND MATHEMATICS

FOUNDATIONS OF SCIENCE: THE PHILOSOPHY OF THEORY AND EXPERIMENT, N. R. Campbell. A critique of the most fundamental concepts of science in general and physics in particular. Examines why certain propositions are accepted without question, demarcates science from philosophy, clarifies the understanding of the tools of science. Part One analyzes the presuppositions of scientific thought: existence of the material world, nature of scientific laws, multiplication of probabilities, etc.: Part Two covers the nature of experiment and the application of mathematics: conditions for measurement, relations between numerical laws and theories, laws of error, etc. An appendix covers problems arising from relativity, force, motion, space, and time. A classic in its field. Index. xiii + 565pp. 5⅝ x 8⅜.
S372 Paperbound **$2.95**

THE NATURE OF PHYSICAL THEORY, P. W. Bridgman. Here is how modern physics looks to a highly unorthodox physicist—a Nobel laureate. Pointing out many absurdities of science, and demonstrating the inadequacies of various physical theories, Dr. Bridgman weighs and analyzes the contributions of Einstein, Bohr, Newton, Heisenberg, and many others. This is a non-technical consideration of the correlation of science and reality. Index. xi + 138pp. 5⅝ x 8.
S33 Paperbound **$1.25**

THE VALUE OF SCIENCE, Henri Poincaré. Many of the most mature ideas of the "last scientific universalist" covered with charm and vigor for both the beginning student and the advanced worker. Discusses the nature of scientific truth, whether order is innate in the universe or imposed upon it by man, logical thought versus intuition (relating to math, through the works of Weierstrass, Lie, Klein, Riemann), time and space (relativity, psychological time, simultaneity), Hertz's concept of force, interrelationship of mathematical physics to pure math, values within disciplines of Maxwell, Carnot, Mayer, Newton, Lorentz, etc. Index. iii + 147pp. 5⅝ x 8.
S469 Paperbound **$1.35**

SCIENCE AND HYPOTHESIS, Henri Poincaré. Creative psychology in science. How such concepts as number, magnitude, space, force, classical mechanics were developed, and how the modern scientist uses them in his thought. Hypothesis in physics, theories of modern physics. Introduction by Sir James Larmor. "Few mathematicians have had the breadth of vision of Poincaré, and none is his superior in the gift of clear exposition," E. T. Bell. Index. 272pp. 5⅝ x 8.
S221 Paperbound **$1.35**

PHILOSOPHY AND THE PHYSICISTS, L. S. Stebbing. The philosophical aspects of modern science examined in terms of a lively critical attack on the ideas of Jeans and Eddington. Discusses the task of science, causality, determinism, probability, consciousness, the relation of the world of physics to that of everyday experience. Probes the philosophical significance of the Planck-Bohr concept of discontinuous energy levels, the inferences to be drawn from Heisenberg's Uncertainty Principle, the implications of "becoming" involved in the 2nd law of thermodynamics, and other problems posed by the discarding of Laplacean determinism. 285pp. 5⅝ x 8.
T480 Paperbound **$1.65**

THE PHILOSOPHICAL WRITINGS OF PEIRCE, edited by Justus Buchler. (Formerly published as THE PHILOSOPHY OF PEIRCE.) This is a carefully balanced exposition of Peirce's complete system, written by Peirce himself. It covers such matters as scientific method, pure chance vs. law, symbolic logic, theory of signs, pragmatism, experiment, and other topics. Introduction by Justus Buchler, Columbia University. xvi + 368pp. 5⅝ x 8.
T217 Paperbound **$2.00**

LANGUAGE, TRUTH AND LOGIC, A. Ayer. A clear introduction to the Vienna and Cambridge schools of Logical Positivism. It sets up specific tests by which you can evaluate validity of ideas, etc. Contents: Function of philosophy, elimination of metaphysics, nature of analysis, a priori, truth and probability, etc. 10th printing. "I should like to have written it myself," Bertrand Russell. Index. 160pp. 5⅝ x 8.
T10 Paperbound **$1.25**

MATHEMATICS AND SCIENCE: LAST ESSAYS (DERNIÈRES PENSÉES), Henri Poincaré. Translated by J. W. Bolduc. A posthumous volume of articles and lectures by the great French mathematician, philosopher, scientist. Here are nine pieces, never before translated into English, on such subjects as The Evolution of Laws, Space and Time, Space and 3 Dimensions, The Logic of infinity in Mathematics (discussing Russell's theory of types), Mathematics and Logic, The Quantum Theory and its Modern Applications, Relationship Between Matter and Ether, Ethics and Science and The Moral Alliance. First English translation of Dernières Pensées. New index. viii + 128pp. 5⅜ x 8½.
S1101 Paperbound **$1.25**

THE PSYCHOLOGY OF INVENTION IN THE MATHEMATICAL FIELD, J. Hadamard. Where do ideas come from? What role does the unconscious play? Are ideas best developed by mathematical reasoning, word reasoning, visualization? What are the methods used by Einstein, Poincaré, Galton, Riemann? How can these techniques be applied by others? Hadamard, one of the world's leading mathematicians, discusses these and other questions. xiii + 145pp. 5⅝ x 8.
T107 Paperbound **$1.25**

CHEMISTRY AND PHYSICAL CHEMISTRY

ORGANIC CHEMISTRY, F. C. Whitmore. The entire subject of organic chemistry for the practicing chemist and the advanced student. Storehouse of facts, theories, processes found elsewhere only in specialized journals. Covers aliphatic compounds (500 pages on the properties and synthetic preparation of hydrocarbons, halides, proteins, ketones, etc.), alicyclic compounds, aromatic compounds, heterocyclic compounds, organophosphorus and organometallic compounds. Methods of synthetic preparation analyzed critically throughout. Includes much of biochemical interest. "The scope of this volume is astonishing," INDUSTRIAL AND ENGINEERING CHEMISTRY. 12,000-reference index. 2387-item bibliography. Total of x + 1005pp. 5⅜ x 8.
Two volume set.
S700 Vol I Paperbound **$2.00**
S701 Vol II Paperbound **$2.00**
The set **$4.00**

THE MODERN THEORY OF MOLECULAR STRUCTURE, Bernard Pullman. A reasonably popular account of recent developments in atomic and molecular theory. Contents: The Wave Function and Wave Equations (history and bases of present theories of molecular structure); The Electronic Structure of Atoms (Description and classification of atomic wave functions, etc.); Diatomic Molecules; Non-Conjugated Polyatomic Molecules; Conjugated Polyatomic Molecules; The Structure of Complexes. Minimum of mathematical background needed. New translation by David Antin of "La Structure Moléculaire." Index. Bibliography. vii + 87pp. 5⅜ x 8½.
S987 Paperbound **$1.00**

CATALYSIS AND CATALYSTS, Marcel Prettre, Director, Research Institute on Catalysis. This brief book, translated into English for the first time, is the finest summary of the principal modern concepts, methods, and results of catalysis. Ideal introduction for beginning chemistry and physics students. Chapters: Basic Definitions of Catalysis (true catalysis and generalization of the concept of catalysis); The Scientific Bases of Catalysis (Catalysis and chemical thermodynamics, catalysis and chemical kinetics); Homogeneous Catalysis (acid-base catalysis, etc.); Chain Reactions; Contact Masses; Heterogeneous Catalysis (Mechanisms of contact catalyses, etc.); and Industrial Applications (acids and fertilizers, petroleum and petroleum chemistry, rubber, plastics, synthetic resins, and fibers). Translated by David Antin. Index. vi + 88pp. 5⅜ x 8½.
S998 Paperbound **$1.00**

POLAR MOLECULES, Pieter Debye. This work by Nobel laureate Debye offers a complete guide to fundamental electrostatic field relations, polarizability, molecular structure. Partial contents: electric intensity, displacement and force, polarization by orientation, molar polarization and molar refraction, halogen-hydrides, polar liquids, ionic saturation, dielectric constant, etc. Special chapter considers quantum theory. Indexed. 172pp. 5⅜ x 8.
S64 Paperbound **$1.50**

THE ELECTRONIC THEORY OF ACIDS AND BASES, W. F. Luder and Saverio Zuffanti. The first full systematic presentation of the electronic theory of acids and bases—treating the theory and its ramifications in an uncomplicated manner. Chapters: Historical Background; Atomic Orbitals and Valence; The Electronic Theory of Acids and Bases; Electrophilic and Electrodotic Reagents; Acidic and Basic Radicals; Neutralization; Titrations with Indicators; Displacement; Catalysis; Acid Catalysis; Base Catalysis; Alkoxides and Catalysts; Conclusion. Required reading for all chemists. Second revised (1961) eidtion, with additional examples and references. 3 figures. 9 tables. Index. Bibliography xii + 165pp. 5⅜ x 8.
S201 Paperbound **$1.50**

KINETIC THEORY OF LIQUIDS, J. Frenkel. Regarding the kinetic theory of liquids as a generalization and extension of the theory of solid bodies, this volume covers all types of arrangements of solids, thermal displacements of atoms, interstitial atoms and ions, orientational and rotational motion of molecules, and transition between states of matter. Mathematical theory is developed close to the physical subject matter. 216 bibliographical footnotes. 55 figures. xi + 485pp. 5⅜ x 8.
S95 Paperbound **$2.55**

THE PRINCIPLES OF ELECTROCHEMISTRY, D. A. MacInnes. Basic equations for almost every subfield of electrochemistry from first principles, referring at all times to the soundest and most recent theories and results; unusually useful as text or as reference. Covers coulometers and Faraday's Law, electrolytic conductance, the Debye-Hueckel method for the theoretical calculation of activity coefficients, concentration cells, standard electrode potentials, thermodynamic ionization constants, pH, potentiometric titrations, irreversible phenomena, Planck's equation, and much more. "Excellent treatise," AMERICAN CHEMICAL SOCIETY JOURNAL. "Highly recommended," CHEMICAL AND METALLURGICAL ENGINEERING. 2 Indices. Appendix. 585-item bibliography. 137 figures. 94 tables. ii + 478pp. 5⅝ x 8⅜.
S52 Paperbound **$2.45**

THE PHASE RULE AND ITS APPLICATION, Alexander Findlay. Covering chemical phenomena of 1, 2, 3, 4, and multiple component systems, this "standard work on the subject" (NATURE, London), has been completely revised and brought up to date by A. N. Campbell and N. O. Smith. Brand new material has been added on such matters as binary, tertiary liquid equilibria, solid solutions in ternary systems, quinary systems of salts and water. Completely revised to triangular coordinates in ternary systems, clarified graphic representation, solid models, etc. 9th revised edition. Author, subject indexes. 236 figures. 505 footnotes, mostly bibliographic. xii + 494pp. 5⅜ x 8.
S91 Paperbound **$2.45**

THE SOLUBILITY OF NONELECTROLYTES, Joel H. Hildebrand and Robert L. Scott. The standard work on the subject; still indispensable as a reference source and for classroom work. Partial contents: The Ideal Solution (including Raoult's Law and Henry's Law, etc.); Nonideal Solutions; Intermolecular Forces; The Liquid State; Entropy of Athermal Mixing; Heat of Mixing; Polarity; Hydrogen Bonding; Specific Interactions; "Solvation" and "Association"; Systems of Three or More Components; Vapor Pressure of Binary Liquid Solutions; Mixtures of Gases; Solubility of Gases in Liquids; of Liquids in Liquids; of Solids in Liquids; Evaluation of Solubility Parameters; and other topics. Corrected republication of third (revised) edition. Appendices. Indexes. 138 figures. 111 tables. 1 photograph. iv + 488pp. 5⅜ x 8½.
S1125 Paperbound **$2.50**

TERNARY SYSTEMS: INTRODUCTION TO THE THEORY OF THREE COMPONENT SYSTEMS, G. Masing. Furnishes detailed discussion of representative types of 3-components systems, both in solid models (particularly metallic alloys) and isothermal models. Discusses mechanical mixture without compounds and without solid solutions; unbroken solid solution series; solid solutions with solubility breaks in two binary systems; iron-silicon-aluminum alloys; allotropic forms of iron in ternary system; other topics. Bibliography. Index. 166 illustrations. 178pp. 5⅜ x 8⅜.
S631 Paperbound **$1.50**

THE KINETIC THEORY OF GASES, Leonard B. Loeb, University of California. Comprehensive text and reference book which presents full coverage of basic theory and the important experiments and developments in the field for the student and investigator. Partial contents: The Mechanical Picture of a Perfect Gas, The Mean Free Path—Clausius' Deductions, Distribution of Molecular Velocities, discussions of theory of the problem of specific heats, the contributions of kinetic theory to our knowledge of electrical and magnetic properties of molecules and its application to the conduction of electricity in gases. New 14-page preface to Dover edition by the author. Name, subject indexes. Six appendices. 570-item bibliography. xxxvi + 687pp. 5⅜ x 8½.
S942 Paperbound **$2.95**

IONS IN SOLUTION, Ronald W. Gurney. A thorough and readable introduction covering all the fundamental principles and experiments in the field, by an internationally-known authority. Contains discussions of solvation energy, atomic and molecular ions, lattice energy, transferral of ions, interionic forces, cells and half-cells, transference of electrons, exchange forces, hydrogen ions, the electro-chemical series, and many other related topics. Indispensable to advanced undergraduates and graduate students in electrochemistry. Index. 45 illustrations. 15 tables. vii + 206pp. 5⅜ x 8½.
S124 Paperbound **$1.50**

IONIC PROCESSES IN SOLUTION, Ronald W. Gurney. Lucid, comprehensive examination which brings together the approaches of electrochemistry, thermodynamics, statistical mechanics, electroacoustics, molecular physics, and quantum theory in the interpretation of the behavior of ionic solutions—the most important single work on the subject. More extensive and technical than the author's earlier work (IONS IN SOLUTION, it is a middle-level text for graduate students and researchers in electrochemistry. Covers such matters as Brownian motion in liquids, molecular ions in solution, heat of precipitation, entropy of solution, proton transfers, dissociation constant of nitric acid, viscosity of ionic solutions, etc. 78 illustrations. 47 tables. Name and subject index. ix + 275pp. 5⅜ x 8½.
S134 Paperbound **$1.75**

CRYSTALLOGRAPHIC DATA ON METAL AND ALLOY STRUCTURES, Compiled by A. Taylor and B. J. Kagle, Westinghouse Research Laboratories. Unique collection of the latest crystallographic data on alloys, compounds, and the elements, with lattice spacings expressed uniformly in absolute Angstrom units. Gathers together previously widely-scattered data from the Power Data File of the ATSM, structure reports, and the Landolt-Bornstein Tables, as well as from other original literature. 2300 different compounds listed in the first table, Alloys and Intermetallic Compounds, with much vital information on each. Also listings for nearly 700 Borides, Carbides, Hydrides, Oxides, Nitrides. Also all the necessary data on the crystal structure of 77 elements. vii + 263pp. 5⅜ x 8.
S1013 Paperbound **$2.25**

MATHEMATICAL CRYSTALLOGRAPHY AND THE THEORY OF GROUPS OF MOVEMENTS, Harold Hilton. Classic account of the mathematical theory of crystallography, particularly the geometrical theory of crystal-structure based on the work of Bravais, Jordan, Sohncke, Federov, Schoenflies, and Barlow. Partial contents: The Stereographic Projection, Properties Common to Symmetrical and Asymmetrical Crystals, The Theory of Groups, Coordinates of Equivalent Points, Crystallographic Axes and Axial Ratios, The Forms and Growth of Crystals, Lattices and Translations, The Structure-Theory, Infinite Groups of Movements, Triclinic and Monoclinic Groups, Orthorhombic Groups, etc. Index. 188 figures. xii + 262pp. 5⅜ x 8½.
S1058 Paperbound **$2.00**

CLASSICS IN THE THEORY OF CHEMICAL COMBINATIONS. Edited by O. T. Benfey. Vol. I of the Classics of Science Series, G. Holton, Harvard University, General Editor. This book is a collection of papers representing the major chapters in the development of the valence concept in chemistry. Includes essays by Wöhler and Liebig, Laurent, Williamson, Frankland, Kekulé and Couper, and two by van't Hoff and le Bel, which mark the first extension of the valence concept beyond its purely numerical character. Introduction and epilogue by Prof. Benfey. Index. 9 illustrations. New translation of Kekulé paper by Benfey. xiv + 191pp. 5⅜ x 8½.
S1066 Paperbound **$1.85**

Catalogue of Dover Books

THE CHEMISTRY OF URANIUM: THE ELEMENT, ITS BINARY AND RELATED COMPOUNDS, J. J. Katz and E. Rabinowitch. Vast post-World War II collection and correlation of thousands of AEC reports and published papers in a useful and easily accessible form, still the most complete and up-to-date compilation. Treats "dry uranium chemistry," occurrences, preparation, properties, simple compounds, isotopic composition, extraction from ores, spectra, alloys, etc. Much material available only here. Index. Thousands of evaluated bibliographical references. 324 tables, charts, figures. xxi + 609pp. 5⅜ x 8. S757 Paperbound **$2.95**

THE STORY OF ALCHEMY AND EARLY CHEMISTRY, J. M. Stillman. An authoritative, scholarly work, highly readable, of development of chemical knowledge from 4000 B.C. to downfall of phlogiston theory in late 18th century. Every important figure, many quotations. Brings alive curious, almost incredible history of alchemical beliefs, practices, writings of Arabian Prince Oneeyade, Vincent of Beauvais, Geber, Zosimos, Paracelsus, Vitruvius, scores more. Studies work, thought of Black, Cavendish, Priestley, Van Helmont, Bergman, Lavoisier, Newton, etc. Index. Bibliography. 579pp. 5⅜ x 8. S628 Paperbound **$2.45**